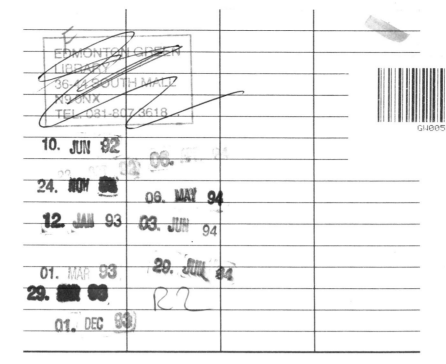

LONDON BOROUGH OF ENFIELD

LIBRARY SERVICES

This item should be RETURNED on or before the latest date stamped.
You may obtain a renewal by personal call, telephone or post. You should
quote the date due for return, the bar code number and your personal
library number. Overdue items will incur charges.

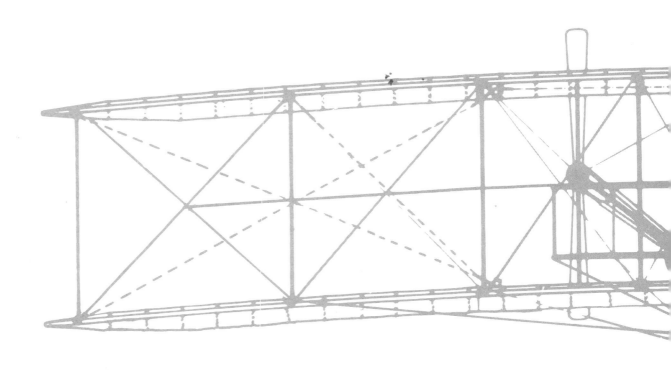

Published for the
National Air and Space Museum
by the
Smithsonian Institution Press
Washington, D.C.   London
1987

The Wright Flyer

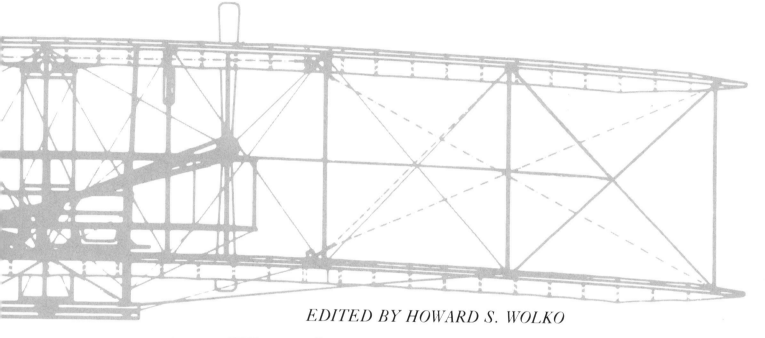

EDITED BY HOWARD S. WOLKO

An Engineering Perspective

Edited by
HOWARD S. WOLKO
Special Advisor for Technology,
Department of Aeronautics
National Air and Space Museum

With Contributions by
JOHN D. ANDERSON, JR.
WALTER J. BOYNE
F.E.C. CULICK
FREDERICK J. HOOVEN
HENRY R. JEX
HARVEY H. LIPPINCOTT
HOWARD S. WOLKO

Library of Congress Cataloging-in-Publication Data
Main entry under title:

The Wright Flyer: an engineering perspective.

   Proceedings of a symposium held at the National
Air and Space Museum, Dec. 16, 1983.

   Contents: The Wright Brothers / John D. Anderson, Jr.
— Aerodynamics, stability, and control of the 1903
Wright Flyer / F.E.C. Culick and H. Jex — Longitudinal
dynamics of the Wright Brothers early Flyers /
Frederick J. Hooven — [etc.]

   Supt. of Docs. no.: SI 9.2:W93/2

   1. Airplanes—Design and construction—Congresses.
2. Wright Flyer (Airplane)—Congresses.   I. Wolko,
Howard S.   II. Anderson, John David.   III. National Air
and Space Museum.

TL671.2.W75   1985   629.133'343   85-600290
ISBN 0-87474-979-4 (pbk.)

British Library Cataloguing in Publication Data is
available

96   95   94   93   92   91   90   89
          5   4   3   2

Edited by Jeanne M. Sexton

The paper in this publication meets the requirements of the
American National Standard for Permanence of Paper for
Printed Materials Z39.48-1984

Unless otherwise noted, information about illustrations can be
obtained from the National Air and Space Museum, Smithsonian
Institution.

Cover: Three-view drawing of the Wright Flyer. (National Air
and Space Museum; gift of the Wright Estate)

Contents

Acknowledgments

The publication of any edited volume depends upon the cooperative efforts of many individuals. The following were of great assistance during preparation of this work. Walter J. Boyne, Director of the National Air and Space Museum, authorized the symposium and encouraged the editor at every stage. E.T. "Tim" Wooldridge, Chairman, Department of Aeronautics of the Museum, provided constant and unfailing cooperation. Claudia Oakes, Associate Curator of Aeronautics, ably attended to all administrative matters. Dr. Tom D. Crouch, Curator of Aeronautics, offered many helpful suggestions. Helen C. McMahon was instrumental in arranging for publication of the work. Special thanks are due Susan L. Owen, who assisted with manuscript preparation.

Foreword

WALTER J. BOYNE

The National Air and Space Museum (NASM) is privileged to be charged with the responsibility to collect, preserve, restore, and exhibit the finest assembly of historic aircraft in the world. At present the collection contains about 300 full-size airplanes. These range from a Lilienthal hang glider of 1894 to the Dassault Falcon 20 fanjet, and include some of the most famous aircraft in the history of flight: *The Spirit of St. Louis*, the *Winnie Mae*, the *Enola Gay*, the Bell X-1, the Curtiss NC-4, the *Vin Fiz*, Amelia Earhart's Vega, Charles and Ann Lindbergh's *Tingmissartoq*—the list goes on.

To single out from this distinguished collection one machine as our most precious possession might be thought impossible. This is not the case. When exhibits for the present NASM building were being selected in the mid-1970s, there was never any doubt as to which airplane would hang as the centerpiece of the entire museum in the most prominent position in the Milestones of Flight gallery which is at the main entrance. What other choice could we have made, other than the 1903 Wright brothers flying machine, the world's first airplane, catalogued, incidentally, as item number 100 among those 300 aircraft.

The story of that machine, and the two men, Wilbur and Orville Wright, who designed, built, and flew it, has been told many times. The sequence of events leading up to the birth of powered flight has justifiably received more study than any other episode in the history of technology.

Yet, for all this attention, the fundamental technological achievements embodied in the design and construction of that machine are still little understood. We find it easy to speak of the engineering genius of Wilbur and Orville Wright, but have difficulty explaining that genius in precise terms.

On December 16, 1983, as part of the National Air and Space Museum's commemoration of the eightieth anniversary of the invention of the airplane, we invited five distinguished engineers to explore with us specific elements of the aerodynamic, structural, and power plant technology incorporated in the 1903 Wright airplane. As we had hoped, the speakers were able to illuminate the approach, methods, and accomplishments of Wilbur and Orville Wright, drawing on their own years of experience in aeronautics.

We offer these papers to you in this volume, edited, annotated, illustrated, and with additional collateral material. I think you will agree that the result is far more than a retelling of the old story; it throws new light upon the epoch-making event of 1903 and the genius of the two bicycle manufacturers whose patience, persistence, and creativity changed the momentum of Mankind's eternal pursuit of greater mobility throughout its environment.

Walter J. Boyne is Director of the National Air and Space Museum. He was formerly Curator of Aeronautics and Chief of Preservation and Restoration at the Museum's Garber Facility.

He was born in East St. Louis, Illinois, in 1929, obtaining his first taste of flying at the Parks Air College Field. He was commissioned in the U.S. Air Force in 1952 and retired as a Colonel in 1974. During his service career he became a Command Pilot, with over 5,000 hours of flying time in a score of different aircraft. He began writing of his primary interest, aviation history, in 1962, and since then has published more than 300 articles, as well as eight books. He is the associate editor of two national magazines, and writes columns for two others.

Mr. Boyne graduated with honors from both the University of California, Berkeley (B.S., B.A.), and the University of Pittsburgh (M.B.A.). Mr. Boyne serves as National Advisor of the American Aviation Historical Society, and is on numerous advisory boards for air and space organizations.

The Wright Brothers
The First True Aeronautical Engineers

JOHN D. ANDERSON, JR.

Introduction

The year 1983 was the eightieth anniversary of the first successful heavier-than-air, powered, manned flight. This historic event, accomplished by Wilbur and Orville Wright on the cold, windswept sand dunes of Kill Devil Hill just outside of Kitty Hawk, North Carolina, took place at approximately 10:35 a.m. on December 17, 1903. This success was the culmination of seven years of hard work, intense dedication, and exceptional engineering insight on the part of the Wrights. One purpose of this paper is to highlight this engineering insight, and to explain why the Wrights succeeded where many others failed. After 1908, when the Wrights first publicly demonstrated their flying machine (Wilbur in France and Orville at Fort Meyer in Virginia), the advancement of aviation took off exponentially. The development of the airplane, and subsequently its transmutation into space vehicles such as the Apollo lunar vehicle and the space shuttle, represents one of the most important contributions of the twentieth century, and will continue to impact all of world society and mankind for the duration of civilization on this planet. There are hundreds of thousands of engineers and scientists today who can trace the origins of their jobs directly back to the Wright brothers, and many millions of others—pilots, airline personnel, travelers, military planners and practitioners—whose lives are touched and frequently dominated by this wonderous invention and development of the "flying machine" by the Wrights. Among other aspects, the profession of aeronautical engineering was born with the success of the Wrights. Orville and Wilbur Wright were essentially the first true aeronautical engineers in history; therefore, a second purpose of this paper is to set forth the reasons for this distinction.

Who invented the concept of the modern airplane? The answer, amazingly enough, is not the Wright brothers. Orville and Wilbur Wright invented the first practical airplane, but the concept of the modern airplane as a machine with fixed wings, a fuselage, and horizonal and vertical tails was introduced long before the Wrights were born. Indeed, the Wrights inherited a certain technology base in aeronautics that had been accumulating for centuries. Another purpose of this paper is to survey pre-Wright aeronautics and to assess its impact on the ultimate success of the Wrights.

Aeronautical Technology before the Wrights

For a moment, imagine that you have been born and raised on an isolated island in the South Pacific, completely devoid of all modern knowledge and technology. However, through the observation of the flight of birds, let us say that you have developed an intense interest in flight. Indeed, you want to fly yourself. How are you going to do it? Are you going to conceive a machine with fixed wings, fuselage, and a tail, with some type of separate mechanism for propulsion? Not likely! Rather, you would be more

1

inclined to directly emulate the birds. Most probably you would fashion wings out of feathers, leaves and branches, or wood, attach them to your arms, climb a hill or a roof, and jump off, flapping wildly. Indeed, this is precisely what ancient man did. Early history is full of accounts of such attempts. Aviation historians have labeled these intrepid people as "tower jumpers." They were uniformly unsuccessful. And, most likely, so would be you in your attempts.

After a number of bumps and bruises, to say the least, you might decide to try a different tactic. You might design a machine which, by means of pushing and pulling levers with your legs and arms, would mechanically flap wings for possible lift and propulsion. Such devices were designed in the past and are called "ornithopters." Perhaps the most spectacular early ornithopter designs were conceived by Leonardo da Vinci (1452–1519), an example of which is shown in Figure 1. This sketch is taken directly from da Vinci's notes, which were only recently discovered in the late nineteenth century. Unfortunately, ornithopters have little or no redeeming aerodynamic qualities and have been uniformly unsuccessful for manned flight.

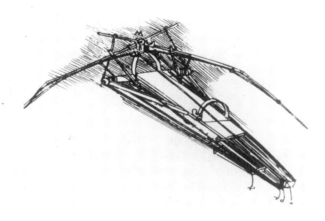

1. An ornithopter design by Leonardo da Vinci, 1486 to 1490.

By this time in your flying endeavors, frustration would most likely set in, as it did for many early would-be aviators. A major glimmer of hope occurred on November 21, 1783, when, for the first time in history, human beings left the ground in a sustained flight through the air. The machine was a hot air balloon designed and built by two French brothers, Joseph and Etienne Montgolfier. On that date, the Montgolfier balloon carried two passengers, Pilatre de Rozier and the Marquis d'Arlande for a 25 minute drifting flight across the spires and roofs of Paris. Although the advent of the hot air balloon, and the hydrogen-filled balloon after it, did much to spark the

2. The first aerial voyage in history: The Montgolfier hot air balloon lifts from the ground near Paris, November 21, 1783.

general public's interest in flight (indeed, the balloon craze of the late eighteenth century can be seen in the enormous number of balloon scenes appearing on porcelain, patterns, and paintings from that period), it did little to advance the technology for heavier-than-air flight.

How then did the concept of the modern airplane—a machine with fixed wings, fuselage, and tail, with separate mechanisms for the production of lift and propulsion—arrive? The answer, in this author's opinion, is through a stroke of genius on the part of one man—George Cayley (1773–1857). Cayley was a relatively well-to-do baronet who lived on an estate in Yorkshire, England. An educated man, Cayley spent his life working intensely on engineering, social, and political problems in England. The dominant interest of his life was heavier-than-air flight, and in 1799 he set forth for the first time in history the concept of the modern airplane. He inscribed this concept on a silver disk (Figure 4). At the left, on one side of the disk, we see a flying machine consisting of a large fixed wing, a fuselage below the wing, and a cruciform tail. For propulsion, Cayley was enamored with the idea of paddles—a misguided thought which is not

3. Sir George Cayley (1773–1857).

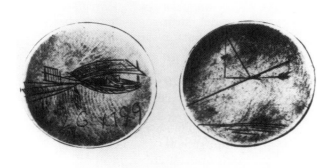

4. The silver disk on which Cayley engraved his concept for a fixed wing aircraft, 1799.

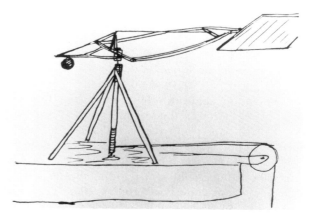

5. Cayley's sketch of his whirling arm apparatus, 1804.

6. Cayley's 1804 glider.

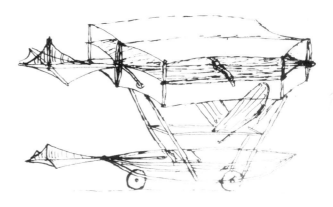

7. Cayley's "boy carrier," 1849.

important in light of his overall concept of the separation of the generation of lift from the generation of propulsion. On the flip side of this disk (the right of Figure 4), we see for the first time in history, an aerodynamic force diagram on a fixed lifting surface at some inclination angle to the oncoming flow. Here, Cayley has clearly identified the drag vector (parallel to the flow) and the lift vector (perpendicular to the flow). Therefore, the concept of the modern airplane was first advanced by George Cayley in 1799. It was this concept which was to be parlayed by the Wright brothers into the first successful airplane more than a century later.

George Cayley did a lot more for aeronautics than just dabble with silver disks. He was the first person

to mount an intelligent, well-conceived program in aeronautical research. In 1804, he built a whirling arm apparatus (Figure 5). At the end of this whirling arm is a lifting surface (a portion of a wing) on which Cayley measured the lift force. Also in 1804, he designed, built, and flew a small model glider (Figure 6). In today's context, such hand-launched gliders are child's play, but in 1804 it represented the first modern configuration airplane in history, with a fixed wing, and a horizontal and vertical tail that could be adjusted. During 1809 and 1810, Cayley published three papers on his aeronautical research where he quite correctly pointed out for the first time that: (1) lift is generated by a region of low pressure on the upper surface of the wing; and (2) cambered wings (curved surfaces) generate lift more efficiently than a flat surface. These results, among many others, can be found in his papers entitled "On Aerial Navigation" published in the November 1809, February 1810, and March 1810 issues of Nicholson's *Journal of Natural Philosophy*. This "triple paper" by Cayley ranks as one of the most important aeronautical documents in history. Cayley went on to put theory into practice. In 1849, he designed, built, and tested a full-size airplane. A triplane (Figure 7), which during some of its tests carried a ten-year-old boy through the air several meters above the ground while gliding downhill. For this reason, the machine is sometimes called "Cayley's boy carrier." One of Cayley's other designs (Figure 8) appeared in *Mechanics' Magazine* in 1852. Cayley never achieved his final goal—sustained heavier-than-air, powered, manned flight. However, he is clearly the grandfather of the modern airplane. (For an entire book on Cayley and his aeronautical contributions, see Reference 1.)

Cayley's concept for an airplane was fixed in the public's eye by a design carried out by William Samuel Henson. Henson's aerial steam carriage embodied Cayley's concepts of a fixed wing, fuselage, and tail. Moreover, it was powered by a steam engine driving two rotating propellers—a propulsion concept infi-

9. **Henson's aerial steam carriage, 1842–1843.**

10. **Stringfellow's almost successful model, 1848.**

nitely more viable than Cayley's flappers. Henson was a contemporary of Cayley's, and his ideas for the steam carriage were published in 1842. The machine was never built, but prints such as that shown in Figure 9 were widely distributed around the world, and served to crystallize in the mind of the general public what an airplane—whenever it would be successful—might look like.

Also contemporary with Cayley, and a friend of Henson's, was John Stringfellow, who made several attempts to bring Henson's design to fruition. For example, he built this almost successful model (Figure 10) in 1848. Stringfellow designed several steam engines for aeronautical use, but all were simply too heavy for the power they produced.

Adding to the list of attempts and failures during the last quarter of the nineteenth century were those of Felix Du Temple and Alexander F. Mozhaiski. Du Temple was a Frenchman who designed and built a flying machine with forward-swept wings (Figure 11). In 1874, at Brest, France, this aircraft achieved

Mechanics' Magazine,

MUSEUM, REGISTER, JOURNAL, AND GAZETTE.

No. 1520.]   SATURDAY, SEPTEMBER 25, 1852.   [Price 3d., Stamped 4d.
Edited by J. C. Robertson, 166, Fleet-street.

SIR GEORGE CAYLEY'S GOVERNABLE PARACHUTES.

Fig. 2.

Fig. 1.

8. **Cayley's 1852 glider.**

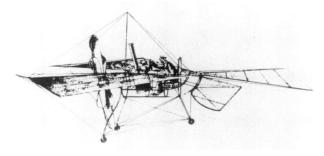

11. **Du Temple's airplane, 1874.**

12. Mozhaiski's airplane, 1884.

the world's first "powered hop" when it was launched down an inclined plane and left the ground for a moment. Ten years later, Mozhaiski in Russia designed and built the aircraft shown in Figure 12. It too was launched down an inclined plane and flew for a few seconds. It represented the second "powered hop" in history. However, neither flight represented anything close to the sustained, controlled flight necessary for success.

The last half of the nineteenth century witnessed a growing list of serious technical achievements in aeronautics. For example, in 1870 the Frenchman Alphonse Pénaud was the first to experiment with rubber-band-powered model aircraft, with which he studied stability and control aspects associated with wing dihedral and various tail incidence angles. One of his model aircraft, the "planophore," is shown in Figure 13. A promising aeronautical career was cut

14. Francis H. Wenham (1824–1908).

gested by Richard Harte in England in 1870 (Figure 15). Harte conceived this device to counteract the torque of a propeller and to act as a differential drag mechanism to steer an airplane in directional flight.

13. Pénaud and his planophore, 1870.

short by Pénaud's suicide in 1880. Also during this period, the Englishman Francis H. Wenham discovered that most of the lift on an airplane wing was obtained from the portion near the leading edge. As a result, in 1866, Wenham was the first person to discuss the benefits of high aspect ratio wings. Wenham went on to design, build, and use the first wind tunnel in history, in 1871. In another development, the use of a flaplike surface at the trailing edge of a wing—today we would call it an aileron—was sug-

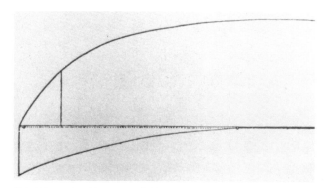

15. Harte's ailerons, 1870.

However, he did not think of this aileron as a roll control device for inducing motion about the airplane's longitudinal axis. The stunning aspect of roll control was left to the Wright brothers to invent. Also during this period the first serious airfoil development was carried out by the Englishman Horatio F. Phillips. Using the second wind tunnel in history, Phillips conducted numerous experiments on double surface airfoils (Figure 16). These airfoil shapes were patented by Phillips—the six upper shapes in 1884 and the

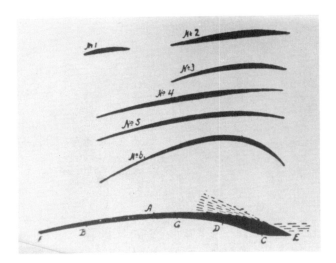

16. Airfoils of Horatio F. Phillips.

lower airfoil in 1891. The Aeronautical Society of Great Britain, formed in 1866, helped to add cohesion and credibility to this aeronautical research. The membership constituted serious researchers with good scientific reputations. It sponsored regular scientific meetings and technical journals. The Society still flourishes today in the form of the highly respected Royal Aeronautical Society, and has been the role model for subsequent societies such as the modern American Institute of Aeronautics and Astronautics in America today.

An interesting figure just before the turn of the century was Sir Hiram Maxim, an American expatriate from Texas living in England. Maxim designed and built a huge steam-powered machine (Figure 17), which perhaps best illustrates the culmination of aeronautical technology of the late nineteenth century. Although it never successfully flew, on July 31, 1894, it did rise above a guide track and ran for a length of 600 feet before being snagged by a guard rail several feet above the track. Maxim's aircraft is a perfect example of what the famed aviation historian Charles H. Gibbs-Smith termed the "chauffeur" philosophy. Simply stated, this philosophy embodied all efforts to get into the air by brute force: give me an engine powerful enough to lift the machine into the air, and I will not worry too much about how to fly it once airborne. I will simply drive it around like a carriage on the ground. This philosophy was uniformly unsuccessful.

In contrast, the "airman's" philosophy was quite different. Here, the approach is to first get up in the air, fly around with gliders, and obtain the "feel" of an airplane *before* putting an engine on the vehicle.

17. Sir Hiram Maxim and his airplane, 1894.

John D. Anderson, Jr.

This "airman's" philosophy was first advanced by the German engineer Otto Lilienthal, who designed and flew the first successful gliders in history. Lilienthal collected a large bulk of aerodynamic data, which he published in 1889 in a book entitled *Der Vogelflug als Grundlage der Fliegekunst* (Bird flight as the basis of aviation). This book greatly influenced aeronautical design for the next 15 years, and was the bible for the early designs of the Wright brothers. During the period 1891—1896, Lilienthal made over 2,500 successful glider flights. With these, he advanced the cause of aeronautics by leaps and bounds. He was a man of aeronautical stature comparable to Cayley and the Wright brothers. Unfortunately, during a glider flight on August 9, 1896, Lilienthal stalled and crashed to the ground. His spine was broken, and he died a day later in a Berlin hospital. There is some feeling that had Lilienthal lived, he might have beaten the Wright brothers to the punch. No one will ever know; however, it is certain that the Wright brothers picked up the "airman's" philosophy from Lilienthal, and as we will soon see, this philosophy ultimately led to success.

As a final note in this section, we mention again that Lilienthal was killed in 1896. The year 1896 is a "red-letter" date in the history of aviation for several other reasons, which will soon be apparent. Please keep 1896 in mind as you read further.

The Race for the First Flight—Langley and the Wright Brothers

By the last decade of the nineteenth century, aeronautical technology had matured far beyond the early "tower jumpers" and ornithopter designs, and indeed by this time the concept originally set forth by George Cayley in 1799 had been refined to the extent that success had to be imminent. This technology base developed during the 1800s was directly inherited by two groups working at the turn of the century in the United States. One group was led by Samuel Pierpont Langley at the Smithsonian Institution, and the other constituted two young brothers in Dayton, Ohio— Wilbur and Orville Wright. Whether they realized it or not, these two groups were in a race for the first powered flight. This section tells their story.

Examine Figure 19. What you see is a photograph of a confident, self-assured, almost pompous man. He is Samuel P. Langley, who in the year 1896 represented, after Lilienthal, probably the most serious and potent aeronautical researcher and designer in the world. Langley was born in Roxbury, Massachu-

18. Otto Lilienthal and one of his gliders.

19. Samuel P. Langley (1834–1906).

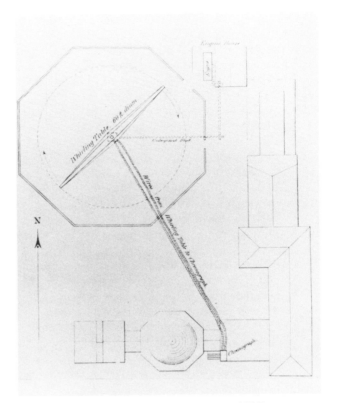

20. Langley's whirling arm apparatus, 1887.

setts, in 1834, and graduated from Boston High School in 1851. He consciously decided not to go to college; rather, he joined an architectural firm in Boston so as to learn civil engineering and architecture in a practical way. He later educated himself in astronomy, and began to travel extensively in Europe. After working a year as an assistant in the Harvard College Observatory in Cambridge, Langley was made an assistant professor of mathematics at the Naval Academy in Annapolis. One year later, in 1867, he became director of the Allegheny Observatory in Pittsburgh. Langley was obviously an upwardly mobile man, and while at the Allegheny Observatory, he made a reputation for himself as a leading expert on sun spots.

In 1885, Langley attended a meeting of the American Association for the Advancement of Science in Buffalo, New York. There he heard a paper on the flight of soaring birds and the technical possibility of manned flight. This paper had a major impact on Langley, and it kindled an interest in flight that burned within Langley's soul to the day he died. Immediately after this meeting, Langley requested and obtained permission from the trustees of the Observatory to build an aeronautical laboratory. He quickly constructed a whirling arm apparatus with which he began to measure the aerodynamic properties of lifting surfaces, much like George Cayley 80 years earlier. This work initiated a decade of intense aeronautical research by Langley. Most of this work,

however, was carried out at the Smithsonian Institution in Washington, D.C., because in 1887 Langley accepted an offer to become the Secretary of the Smithsonian—the most prestigious scientific position in nineteenth-century America. At the Smithsonian, in the original brick building now labeled "the Castle," Langley built an aerodynamic laboratory. There he experimented with nearly a hundred different model airplane configurations, a few of which are shown in Figure 21. This work culminated in a steam-powered, unmanned, heavier-than-air machine which he called an "aerodrome." It was a tandem-wing design, about 16 feet in length. Langley mounted this aerodrome on a catapult on top of a houseboat and, on May 6, 1896, on a wide portion of the Potomac river near Quantico, Virginia, the aerodrome was launched. It flew under its own power for one and a half minutes, covering a distance of over a half mile. It was the first successful sustained flight of a heavier-than-air, powered vehicle in history. A smashing accomplishment for which Langley deserves more accolades than modern aviation history usually accords him. Again, on November 28 of the same year, the aerodrome flew almost two minutes, covering approximately a mile. Elated with his success, Langley felt he had accomplished his goal—to demonstrate the feasibility of powered flight. After ten years of hard effort, extensive research, and considerable expenditure of resources and money, Langley wrote the

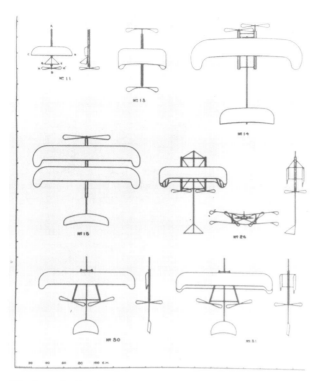

21. Langley's airplane models.

22. Langely's small-scale aerodrome, 1896.

following:

> I have brought to a close the portion of the work which seemed specially mine. For the next state, the commercial and practical development of the idea, it is probable that the world may look to others.

Note the year of Langley's success, 1896—the same year as Otto Lilienthal's death.

Also in this same year, 1896, Wilbur Wright became serious about powered flight. He shortly interested his brother Orville in an endeavor which was to become

23. Langley's aerodrome mounted on the houseboat, 1896.

24. Langley's small-scale aerodrome in flight. These pictures were taken by Alexander Graham Bell, inventor of the telephone and close friend of Langley's, 1896.

the consuming passion for the rest of their lives. Wilbur (born in 1867) and his younger brother, Orville (born in 1871), were members of a family which put much emphasis on intellectual achievement, a dedicated work ethic, high ethical behavior, and modesty. These personal traits, present in Wilbur and Orville to an almost excessive amount, are among the primary reasons for the ultimate success of the Wrights. Their mother had a college degree in mathematics, a very unusual achievement for that day. Their father was a bishop in the United Brethren Church, a very accomplished man who had published books and articles, and who held various administrative positions in the church. As a matter of interest, neither Wilbur nor Orville officially received a high school diploma: Wilbur was not able to attend his commencement exercises (a requirement to obtain his degree), and Orville took a special series of courses in his senior year that did not lead to a prescribed degree. Like Langley, they did not have a formal college education; they were self-made men.

The Wright brothers began their aeronautical work by reading all the available literature, thereby absorbing the aeronautical technology described in the previous section. In particular, they concentrated on a book entitled *Progress in Flying Machines*, published in 1894 by Octave Chanute, a widely respected American civil engineer who became an intense proponent of powered flight during the last part of the nineteenth century. The Wrights also became familiar with the details of Otto Lilienthal's aerodynamic data, and used these data in their first two glider designs. In 1899, after observing the soaring flight of large birds, Wilbur conceived the idea of bending, or deflecting, the tips of wings to achieve lateral control around the longitudinal axis of an aircraft. This concept, popularly called wing warping, was another one of the major ingredients for the Wrights' success.

The Wrights were airmen in the great tradition of Lilienthal. In 1900 they designed, built, and experimented with a glider at Kitty Hawk, North Carolina. This aircraft (Figure 27) had a 17-foot wingspan, a

25. Wilbur Wright (1867–1912).

26. Orville Wright (1871–1948).

John D. Anderson, Jr.

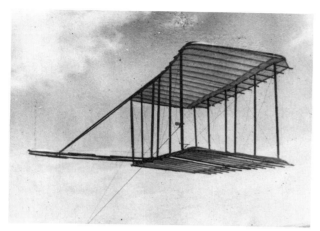

27. Wright brothers' 1900 glider.

28. Wright brothers' 1901 glider.

29. Manly (left) and Langley.

personal backing) offered Langley a $50,000 contract to build a single man-carrying, powered flying machine. Langley accepted. He hired as an assistant Charles Manly, a graduate fresh from Cornell's Sibley School of Mechanical Engineering. For all practical purposes, Langley theorized that he needed only to

horizontal elevator in front of the wings, and was usually flown on strings from the ground. Only a few brief piloted flights were made, mainly because the glider did not perform to the Wrights' expectations. The glider contained the best state-of-the-art aeronautical technology for that day, but it simply did not fly right. It produced far less lift than calculated by the Wrights, and, therefore, had to be flown at a higher angle-of-attack and/or in the face of higher winds than expected. In 1901, the Wrights returned to Kitty Hawk. They had redesigned their glider, this time making it larger with a 22-foot wingspan. Again, the new glider embodied the best aeronautical state-of-the-art, and again the Wrights were not satisfied with its performance. Indeed, on the train returning to Dayton after their 1901 trials, Wilbur is quoted as stating in a moment of despair that "nobody will fly for a thousand years."

Meanwhile, back in Washington, Langley's self-imposed retirement from aeronautical research was short-lived. In 1898, spurred by the Spanish-American War, the War Department (with President McKinley's

30. Manly's engine, the first radial engine in aeronautical history.

scale his previously successful aerodrome to full size. However, he wisely made the decision to switch from steam power to a gasoline-fueled internal combustion engine. Moreover, he calculated that, as a minimum, he needed an engine that could produce 12 horsepower and weigh 100 pounds or less—a horsepower to weight ratio larger than any existing engine of that day. Langley gave a subcontract to the Balzer Company in New York to design and manufacture such an engine—the company went bankrupt trying. Manly then personally took over the engine design, and by 1901 had assembled a radically designed five cylinder radial engine that weighed only 124 pounds and produced a phenomenal 52.4 horsepower. This engine (Figure 30) was to be the best airplane power plant designed until the middle of World War I. In June 1901, Langley tested a quarter-scale gasoline-powered, unmanned aerodrome, which flew perfectly (Figure 31). At this stage, Langley was literally and figuratively "cooking with gas."

31. Langley's gasoline-powered quarter-scale aerodrome, 1901.

Meanwhile, back at Dayton, the Wrights overcame their despair about their disappointing 1901 glider performance. At this stage, they made a decision which took great intellectual courage. To this date, they had faithfully relied upon detailed aerodynamic data published by both Lilienthal and Langley. Now they wondered about its accuracy. Wilbur wrote that "having set out with absolute faith in the existing scientific data, we were driven to doubt one thing after another, until finally, after two years of experiment, we cast it all aside, and decided to rely entirely upon our own investigations." This momentous change in philosophy is one of the major reasons for the Wright brothers' ultimate success. Besides courage, it took a great deal of self-confidence—hallmarks of the Wrights. Between September 1901 and August 1902, the Wrights undertook a major program of aeronautical research. They built a wind tunnel in their bicycle shop in Dayton, where they tested more than 200 different airfoil and wing shapes, some of which are shown in Figure 33. This period of aeronautical research was a high-water mark in early aviation development. With their new-found data,

32. Wright brothers' wind tunnel, 1901–1902.

the Wrights designed a new glider, and in 1902, at Kill Devil Hill, this machine flew very successfully. Figure 34 is one of many photographs taken of their successful 1902 machine—it shows a graceful flight of the most successful glider developed to that point in history. Note the degree of wing warping clearly evident. During 1902, the Wrights made over 1,000 glider flights. They set a distance record of 622.5 feet

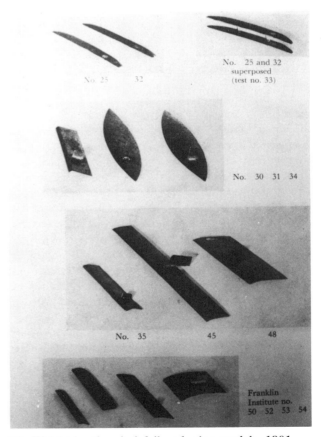

33. Wright brothers' airfoil and wing models, 1901–1902.

John D. Anderson, Jr.

34. Wright brothers' 1902 glider.

and a duration record of 26 seconds. Moreover, they had control about all three axes of the aircraft, which allowed them to make smooth, banked turns. In the process, both Wilbur and Orville became highly skilled and proficient pilots, each achieving more than an hour and a half of flight time. The Wright brothers were carrying the "airman" philosophy to its natural conclusion. Flushed with success, the Wrights returned to Dayton in the fall of 1902, ready for the final step—the inclusion of a power plant.

Once again, the Wrights did everything themselves. Splitting responsibilities, Wilbur tackled the problem of the propeller, and Orville set about to obtain an engine. At first thought, Wilbur assumed that he could find the necessary design information on propellers in the Dayton library—after all, steamships had been using water screws for almost a century. He was disappointed to find only empirical design data which applied to ships, and which were useless for aeronautical application. This situation prompted Wilbur to do his own work. In the process, he developed the first rational airplane propeller theory in history. He was the first to recognize that a propeller is nothing more than a twisted wing, where the "lift" force is now pointing forward for propulsion. Using his theory in conjunction with their airfoil data measured during the previous year, Wilbur designed and constructed a remarkably efficient propeller. This aspect of the Wright brothers' technology is sometimes not fully appreciated, yet it was one of the most important technical victories that led to their success.

In parallel, Orville's first effort on the engine was to inquire with the existing motor manufacturers about the possibility of delivering an engine that could produce 12 horsepower and weigh less than 150 pounds. The responses were uniformly negative. Hence, following in their tradition, Orville, with the aid of their bicycle mechanic, Charlie Taylor, designed and built an original engine that just met their minimum specifications. It was not nearly as impressive as Charles Manly's engine for Langley's aerodrome, but it was sufficient for the job.

With their engine and propeller development behind them, the Wright brothers constructed a new machine from scratch during the summer of 1903. Popularly called the Wright Flyer, it closely resembled the 1902 glider, but had a larger wingspan of 40 feet, 4 inches, and used a double rudder behind the wings and a double elevator in front of the wings. A photograph of this machine, with its engine and twin pusher propellers, is shown in Figure 35. This pho-

35. The 1903 flying machine, popularly called the Wright Flyer.

tograph was taken during the early fall of 1903 at Kill Devil Hill, where the Wrights were making preparations for a powered flight.

Meanwhile, back at the Smithsonian, Langley was also making preparations. His full-scale aerodome was ready. Manly had volunteered to be the pilot, over Langley's objections. Langley's original plans were to first test the aerodrome with a lifeless dummy aboard, but Manly successfully argued that too much money and time had already been spent on their project, and that the schedule for a manned flight could be delayed no longer. Therefore, on October 7, 1903, Langley's aerodrome, mounted on a bigger and better houseboat in the Potomac, was ready for flight. The launching was given wide advance publicity, and the press was present to watch what might be the first successful flight in history. What happened next is described in the resulting report as it appeared in the *Washington Post* the next day:

A few yards from the houseboat were the boats of the reporters, who for three months had been stationed at Widewater. The newspapermen waved their hands. Manly looked down and smiled. [Author's note: Why Manly was smiling is not easy to understand. Here was a man, ready to fly, with *zero* flight time. Both Langley and Manly were "chauffeurs." But let us go on with this newspaper account.] Then his face hardened as he braced himself for the flight, which might have in store for him fame or death. The propeller wheels, a foot from his head, whined around him one thousand times to the minute. A man forward fired two skyrockets. There came answering "toot, toot" from

the tugs. A mechanic stooped, cut the cable holding the catapult; there was a roaring, grinding noise—and the Langley airship tumbled over the edge of the houseboat and disappeared in the river, sixteen feet below. It simply slid into the water like a handful of mortar . . . .

37. Langley's first launch, October 7, 1903.

Manly was unhurt. Langley believed the airplane was fouled by the launching mechanism, and he tried again on December 8, 1903. Again, Manly was at the

36. Langley's full-scale aerodrome on the houseboat, 1903.

38. Langley's second launch, December 8, 1903.

John D. Anderson, Jr.

controls. A dramatic photograph taken a moment after this second launch shows the aerodrome going through a 90 degree angle-of-attack, with its rear wings totally collapsed. Again, Manly was fished out, fortunately unhurt. But this was the end of Langley's attempts.

In light of today's massive government-sponsored aerospace research and development program, it is important to note that the $50,000 War Department contract given to Langley at the turn of the century was the first of its type. Moreover, Langley had utilized an additional $23,000 in Smithsonian resources to help design and construct the aerodrome. As a result, Langley's failures had a rather adverse impact on the political thinking of that day towards government-sponsored research. For example, James A. Hemenway, chairman of the House Appropriations Committee, stated:

> If it is to cost us $73,000 to construct a mud duck that will not fly 50 feet, how much is it going to cost to construct a real flying machine?

Representative Robinson of Indiana had this to say:

> Langley is a professor, wandering in his dreams of flight, who was given to building castles in the air . . . . If steps are not taken to curb research spending, someone will influence some Department to test the principle of erecting buildings beginning with the roof.

Representative Hitchcock of Nebraska, when interviewed by a Brooklyn newspaper, exclaimed:

> You tell Langley for me that the only thing he ever made to fly was Government money!

Finally, from the official War Department report on the entire project:

> We are still far from the ultimate goal, and it would seem as if years of constant work and study by experts, together with the expenditure of thousands of dollars, would still be necessary before we can hope to produce an apparatus of practical utility on these lines.

Nine days after Langley's second failure, the Wright Flyer rose from the sands of Kill Devil Hill.

In retrospect, the vilification of Langley by the press, the public, and government officials was much too harsh. Langley died in 1906, a broken man. He had made a valiant try, and he had exerted all his scientific knowledge and insight to accomplish his goal. He simply had not been able to design the right system—something that the Wright brothers understood much more fully than Langley. However, the successful flights of Langley's small aerodrome represented major aeronautical accomplishments for that period. For these, Langley should be given due credit.

Let us turn again to the Wright brothers. After the development of their propellers and engine, and after constructing their new machine, the Wrights returned to Kill Devil Hill in September 1903. Due to a

combination of bad weather and engine shaft failure, they were delayed far into the fall. Wilbur and Orville had originally planned to fly their new machine first as an unpowered glider in order to get the feel of its flying qualities. However, with their long delays, and due to their intense desire to fly that year, they made a decision somewhat uncharacteristic of their normally conservative, careful approach: they decided that their first flight would be powered.

Their first opportunity finally arrived on December 14. The brothers flipped a coin to see who should be the first pilot. Wilbur won. The Flyer, under power, took off, suddenly went into a steep climb, stalled, and thumped back to the ground. It was the first recorded case of pilot error in powered flight: Wilbur admitted that he put on too much elevator and brought the nose too high. (Had the Wrights been able to follow their original plans to fly the machine as a glider first, then most likely Wilbur would not have overcontrolled, and the first successful powered flight would have gone on the record books on December 14 with Wilbur as the pilot.) A photograph of the aircraft just after Wilbur's attempt shows some slight damage to the canard surfaces in front of the wing (Figure 39).

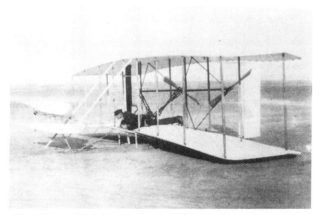

39. Wilbur Wright, moments after his first attempted powered flight, December 14, 1903.

This damage was repaired in a matter of days, and the Flyer was again ready for flight on December 17. This time it was Orville's turn at the controls. It was a cold, windy day, almost too windy for flying. Again, the Wrights were taking an uncharacteristic risk. At 10:35 a.m. the restraining rope was released, and the machine began to move. Figure 40 tells the rest of the story. It is the most famous photograph in the history of aviation. It shows the Wright Flyer at the moment of liftoff, with Wilbur running along side to keep the wing tip from dragging in the sand. The epoch-making flight lasted for 12 seconds and covered 120 feet. It was, in Orville's words, "the first in the history of the world in which a machine carrying a

40. December 17, 1903.

man had raised itself by its own power into the air in full flight, and sailed forward without reduction of speed, and had finally landed at a point as high as that from which it started." There were three more flights that day, the last remaining in the air for 59 seconds and covering 852 feet. The world of powered, manned, heavier-than-air flight—and along with it the world of successful aeronautical engineering—had been born.

Concluding Remarks

Wilbur and Orville Wright were indeed the first *true* aeronautical engineers in history for the following reasons:

1. They were the first to fully recognize the importance of flight control around all three axis of the airplane. Their concept of wing warping for lateral control was pioneering—it distinguished them from all prior inventors, and set them ahead of all contemporary aviators for a decade.

2. They were the first to modify and improve their flight controls by means of a systematic series of successful glider flights in 1902. In this vein, they might even be labeled the first true test pilots as well.

3. They were the first to use wind tunnel results to correct some defective data existing in the literature. Moreover, although they never tested a full airplane configuration in their tunnel, their wind tunnel models were directly aimed at optimizing a specific flight configuration. Therefore, the Wrights were the first to use a wind tunnel in the modern mode that we see today.

4. The Wrights' understanding of the true aerodynamic function of a propeller, and their subsequent development of a propeller theory are important firsts in the history of aeronautical engineering. This work sets them apart from any previous investigators.

5. The fact that the Wrights, with no prior experience with any type of internal combustion engine, were able to design and build a successful engine that was beyond the state-of-the-art, and to accomplish this in the space of six months, is truly amazing.

6. Finally, and probably most importantly, the Wrights were the first to treat a flying machine as an *integrated system* involving aerodynamics, propulsion, structures, and flight dynamics. They fully appreciated the interaction and mutual importance of all these aspects. In this sense, they were the first to build a *total* flying machine—a machine which had all the major aspects that a modern airplane has today.

John D. Anderson, Jr.

The above reasons, based on their technology, account for the Wright brothers' success. However, there are other, more philosophical reasons why the Wright brothers succeeded where others failed. First, they had an intense work ethic which was brought into focus day and night, day after day, towards their goal. Second, they were supremely self-confident, never really doubting the value of their final goal. Third, they were intellectually courageous, willing to do things on their own when the existing technology either failed them, or did not measure up to their requirements. Moreover, they had the insight to recognize good technology from bad technology. Finally, without the benefit of a formal education, the Wright brothers had an innate sense of engineering—very systematic minds that logically and inexorably led them to success.

This article has set the stage for the papers that follow. In these papers, you will have the opportunity to probe deeply into the technology of the Wright brothers. You will be amazed to observe how sound that technology was. You will be swamped with the realization that their technology was not by chance or happenstance—they were truly the first aeronautical engineers.

As a final note, if you are interested in reading more extensively about the early development of aeronautics from antiquity to the Wright brothers, there are numerous books that treat the subject. References 1–8 are just a few of the many which you may find of particular interest. It is from these books that much of the material in this article was gleaned.

John D. Anderson, Jr. is a leading engineering educator. A native of Lancaster, Pennsylvania, he is a graduate of the University of Florida and holds a Ph.D. in Aeronautical and Astronautical Engineering from Ohio State University. He has served as a task scientist with the U.S. Air Force at the Aerospace Research Laboratory at Wright Patterson AFB and as Chief of the Hypersonics Group, Aerophysics Division at the Naval Ordnance Laboratory at White Oaks, Maryland. Since 1973 he has been a Professor of Engineering at the University of Maryland and was Chairman of that Department from 1973 to 1980. He has published over 70 technical papers and is the author of three books.

Dr. Anderson is a member of Tau Beta Pi, Sigma Xi, Sigma Tau, American Physical Society, and the American Society for Engineering Education. He is an Associate Fellow of the American Institute of Aeronautics and Astronautics and a Fellow of the Washington Academy of Sciences. In 1975, he was chosen an Outstanding Educator of America, and won the Engineering Sciences Award of the Washington Academy of Science. He is listed in *Who's Who in America* and has been designated by the University of Maryland as a Distinguished Scholar/Teacher.

References

1. Gibbs-Smith, Charles H. *Sir George Cayley's Aeronautics: 1796–1855*. London: Her Majesty's Stationery Office, 1962.

2. *Aviation: An Historical Survey from its Origins to the End of World War II*. London: Her Majesty's Stationery Office, 1970.

3. Josephy, A.M., and Gordon, A. *The American Heritage History of Flight*. New York: Simon and Schuster, 1962.

4. McFarland, Marvin W., ed. *The Papers of Wilbur and Orville Wright*. New York: McGraw-Hill, 1953.

5. Anderson, John D., Jr. *Introduction to Flight: Its Engineering and History*. New York: McGraw-Hill, 1978.

6. Crouch, Tom D. *A Dream of Wings*. New York: W. W. Norton & Co., 1981.

7. Hallion, Richard P., ed. *The Wright Brothers: Heirs of Prometheus*. Washington, D.C.: Smithsonian Institution Press, 1978.

8. Combs, Harry, with Cardin, Martin. *Kill Devil Hill*. Boston: Houghton Mifflin Co., 1979.

9. Vaeth, J. Gordon. *Langley: A Man of Science and Flight*. New York: Ronald Press, 1966.

Aerodynamics, Stability, and Control of the 1903 Wright Flyer

F.E.C. CULICK AND HENRY R. JEX

Introduction

The design, construction, and flight of the 1903 Wright Flyer was a scientific engineering achievement of the first order.[1] It is true, as the Wright brothers thoroughly appreciated, that their first powered flights were really only an intermediate success. They worked for two more years to improve their design until they had a practical airplane. But it is proper that we celebrate December 17, 1903, as the beginning of aviation. By then the Wrights had in hand practically all of the fundamental understanding and knowledge they needed to show the world how to fly.

Even by modern standards, the Wright brothers' program was extraordinarily well-conceived and efficiently executed. They conducted the necessary tests, collected only the data they needed, and generally conducted their work to learn just what they required to succeed. Other papers in this collection will treat the Wrights' work on engines and structures. We restrict our discussion here to aerodynamics, stability, and flight control.

The following pages amount to a progress report covering contributions by many people. In 1953 members of the Los Angeles Section of the American Institute of Aeronautics and Astronautics (AIAA) constructed a reproduction of the 1903 Flyer. That airplane was destroyed in the fire at the San Diego Aerospace Museum in 1977; shortly after that event, the Los Angeles AIAA section received the insurance claim. Mr. Howard Marx of the Northrop Corporation, as chairman of the AIAA committee on special events, proposed that a flying reproduction be constructed.

The idea was enthusiastically supported and the AIAA Wright Flyer Project was born. We set out more than five years ago with dozens of people to do by committee what the Wright brothers alone did in less than four years! And we still haven't flown our "Flyer"!

Our plans have expanded. We now intend to construct two reproductions. One is an accurate full-scale rendition of the 1903 Flyer to be tested in a wind tunnel. It is complete except for covering (Figure 1). The flying reproduction will incorporate small changes from the original design to make the aircraft easier to fly safely. Much of the material covered in this paper will serve as the basis for determining those changes. Equally important is our effort to interpret the Wrights' accomplishments in terms of the knowledge we have gained in the 80 years since their first flight.

We shall describe some of the results obtained from wind tunnel tests of two models, a ⅙ scale model tested at the California Institute of Technology, and a ⅛ scale model tested in a high speed tunnel whose owners will identify themselves at some later date. The data have been analyzed, partly with the help of some theoretical calculations at the Douglas Aircraft Company, to provide firm assessments of the stability and control of the 1903 Flyer. Using modern control theory, analyses carried out at Systems Technology, Inc. have helped us understand how the aircraft actually behaved when the Wright brothers flew it. The results are particularly interesting for the controversial interconnected wing warp/rudder devised by

19

1. Uncovered full-scale 1903 Flyer. (Los Angeles AIAA Wright Flyer Project, 1983)

the Wrights for lateral directional control.

It was not a good airplane but it was by far good enough!

The Wrights' Wind Tunnel Data

Probably the best-known scientific work by the Wrights is their program to obtain data for airfoils and wings. Theirs was not the first wind tunnel—which was invented in England, by Wenham and Browning in 1871 (Reference 3)—nor were theirs the first wind tunnel data obtained in the United States. Albert C. Wells measured the correct value for the drag coefficient of a flat plate, reported in his thesis submitted to the Massachusetts Institute of Technology in 1896 (Reference 4). Wells converted a ventilation duct for his work; the Wrights designed and built a small open circuit tunnel. With that device, during three months in 1901 they took the first extensive systematic data suitable for the design of aircraft. The results served them well for a decade.

Ten years earlier, Otto Lilienthal had used a whirling arm apparatus to measure the lift and drag for various airfoils approximating the shape of birds' wings (Reference 5). The Wright brothers used his data in the design of their 1900 and 1901 gliders. It is a familiar fact that because they obtained substan-

tially less lift with their gliders than they had predicted with Lilienthal's results, the Wrights resolved to obtain their own data. What is less well known is that in the course of their program they determined that Lilienthal's data were essentially correct.

The difficulty lay with the value of a coefficient which was required to convert Lilienthal's numbers to obtain the actual aerodynamic forces acting on a wing. That coefficient—the drag force acting on a unit area of plate oriented perpendicular to a stream moving with speed one mile per hour—was called Smeaton's coefficient.

John Smeaton was the preeminent English civil engineer of the eighteenth century. In 1752 he published an important memoir (Reference 6) in which he discussed theory and experiment for the fluid mechanics of water wheels and windmills. He included a table of data, provided by a Mr. Rouse, from which the coefficient defined above can be deduced and shown to be approximately 0.0049, independent of velocity. Thus the drag on a plate having area S in a stream moving at speed v (MPH) is

$$D = 0.0049V^2S$$

The value 0.0049 is for air, being proportional to the density of the medium. Presumably because of Smeaton's stature and because he authored the book, his name was subsequently attached to this number. Mr. Rouse, who actually did the work, has hardly ever since been cited.

In any case, this value of Smeaton's coefficient persisted for 150 years. The strength of tradition caused Lilienthal to accept the value without question. But the Wrights determined otherwise. With a clever combination of their wind tunnel data and a few tests with a wing from their 1901 gliders, they concluded that the correct value was 0.0033, which is now known to be correct for the range of speeds in which they were working. Samuel P. Langley (Reference 7) had previously found this result, confirmed later by Wells.

Figure 2 shows the close agreement between the measurements of Lilienthal and those of the Wrights for the same parabolic airfoil. They are expressed here in the modern terms, lift coefficient (lift force divided by the dynamic pressure and area) as a function of the angle of incidence between the flow and the airfoil. The shift of the Wrights' view from their initial belief that Lilienthal's data were seriously in error, to the recognition that their own results agreed with his, is a superb illustration of the objective and thoroughly professional fashion in which they carried out their work. The following selections from Wilbur's diary (Reference 1) summarize the development of their views.

October 6, 1901
I am now absolutely certain that Lilienthal's table is very seriously in error, but that the error is not so great as I had previously estimated . . . . If in our Kitty Hawk calculations we had used a coefficient of .0033 instead of .005 the apparent advantage of our surface over the plane as per the Duchemin formula would have been much greater. I see no good reason for using a greater coefficient than .0033.

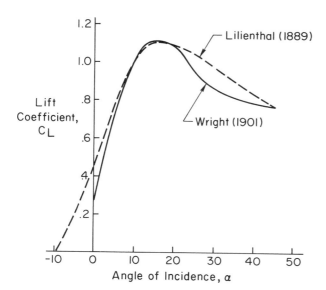

2. Data for lift coefficient versus angle of incidence, Lilienthal and the Wright brothers.

October 16, 1901
It would appear that Lilienthal is very much nearer the truth then we have heretofore been disposed to think.

November 2, 1901
Lilienthal is a little obscure at times but, once understood, there is reason in nearly all he writes.

December 1, 1902
The Lilienthal table has risen very much in my estimation since we began our present series of experiments for determining lift . . . for a surface as near as possible like that described in his book the table is probably as near correct as it is possible to make it with the methods he used.

Thus the Wrights concluded that Lilienthal's data were correct and that the cause of their low prediction of the lift force was the incorrectly high value of Smeaton's coefficient. They never measured the correct value directly, but deduced it from their wind tunnel tests for an airfoil and their small number of measurements for a full-scale wing. Their reasoning, experimental work, and results are all truly remarkable. They are especially impressive when one realizes that this effort was motivated entirely by the practical need to obtain information necessary to the successful design of their aircraft. This is a very early example of a process which is now so common that it is taken for granted. The demands of an engineering program may pose a question which can be satisfactorily answered only by fundamental scientific work completed outside the main thrust of the engineering effort. It was one of the great strengths of the Wrights that they were able to identify, formulate, and solve crucial basic problems. In contrast, their contemporaries trying to build flying machines were able to progress only with crude trial-and-error methods of traditional nineteenth-century engineering and invention. With their philosophy and style the Wright brothers were solidly in the twentieth century, far ahead of their contemporaries in aviation. That is the major reason for their rapid and certain progress to manned flight.

Fundamental Notions of Stability

Nothing related to the Wright brothers has created more confusion, controversy, discussion, and at times vitriolic argument than questions of equilibrium, stability, and control. There is fairly general agreement that the Wrights' experience with bicycles taught them the virtue of control. The bicycle is unstable without active control by the rider. Thus the Wrights were not deterred by the possibility of an unstable vehicle which could nevertheless be successfully operated with practice, providing the means existed for proper control. It is also clear that control was always a central issue during development of their aircraft.[2]

What is by no means evident is the extent to which the Wrights inadvertently produced unstable aircraft. They certainly refused to follow their contemporaries who were preoccupied with the goal of inventing an intrinsically or automatically stable airplane. On the other hand, it is not necessary that an airplane be unstable to be controllable.

The Wrights were the first to place the smaller horizontal surface forward—the canard configuration. They knew very well the history of the aft horizontal tail. In particular, they were aware that, as perceived by Cayley in 1799 and shown by Pénaud in 1872, an aircraft with an aft tail can be made longitudinally stable. Moreover, early in their program, in 1899 with the kite, and in 1900 with the man-carrying kite/glider, they experimented successfully with an aft tail. They knew that the configuration could easily be made stable. There is no doubt that they chose the canard because of fear, first expressed by Wilbur, that the aft tail carried with it an intrinsic danger. What worried them was the possible inability to recover from a stall, due to loss of lift induced by a vertical gust, or by the pilot upon raising the nose too far. That had been the cause of Lilienthal's death in 1896.

At least twice during the tests in 1901, Wilbur found himself in a stalled condition. By manipulating the canard he was able to get the nose down and the aircraft mushed to the ground without serious damage. He was therefore convinced that his reasoning was correct. A certain sense of security was given the pilot because he was able to see the actions of the control surface, which also provided a visual reference relative to the ground.

Thus the choice of the canard configuration, the most distinctive feature of the Wright aircraft, was not based on sound technical grounds of stability. It was rather a matter of control in pitch, especially under extreme conditions. In fact, the Wrights did not understand stability in the precise sense that we do now. The reason is fundamental: nowhere in their work did they consider explicitly the balance of moments.[3] They shared that ignorance with all others trying to build aircraft at that time. So strictly, whether their aircraft were stable or unstable was an accidental matter. Often, changes in a design were made which would change the stability, and not always favorably. But the motivation was always the desire to affect some observable characteristic, such as undulations in pitch. From this point of view, the question of the Wrights' intentions to design an unstable airplane is meaningless.

For our later discussion of the wind tunnel data, it will be helpful to understand the ideas of equilibrium and stability. When an aircraft is in steady motion, there must be no net force or moment acting. For horizontal flight, the vertical lift must exactly equal the weight and the thrust of the propulsion system must be just sufficient to overcome the drag. The symmetry of the aircraft guarantees that there shall be no net side force.

In order that there be no net moment tending to rotate the aircraft, the moments about three axes must separately vanish: the pitch, roll, and yaw moments must all vanish for equilibrium. Much work is saved in practice by using coefficients rather than the moments themselves. A moment coefficient is obtained by dividing the moment by the dynamic pressure; the wing area; and a length, either the wing chord for the pitching moment or the wing span for the roll and yaw moments. The moment coefficients are given the symbols C_l, C_m, and C_n for roll, pitch, and yaw, respectively, as shown in Figure 3.

To ensure equilibrium or trim, the moment coefficients must vanish, $C_l = C_m = C_n = 0$, static condition. Whether or not the equilibrium state is *stable* depends on the changes of the aerodynamic moments when small disturbances are applied to the aircraft. Consider an aircraft in steady horizontal flight. Suppose that a vertical gust causes an increase in the angle of incidence between the flow and the aircraft. The initial equilibrium state may be restored if the increased incidence generates a pitching moment causing the nose to pitch down so as to reduce the angle of incidence to its initial value. By convention,

EQUILIBRIUM(TRIM)	MOMENT = 0
Pitching Moment	$C_m = 0$
Yaw Moment	$C_n = 0$
Roll Moment	$C_l = 0$

STABILITY OF EQUILIBRIUM

When a disturbance is applied(e.g. a gust) the change of aerodynamic moment must be such as to restore equilibrum

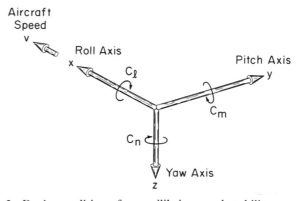

3. Basic conditions for equilibrium and stability.

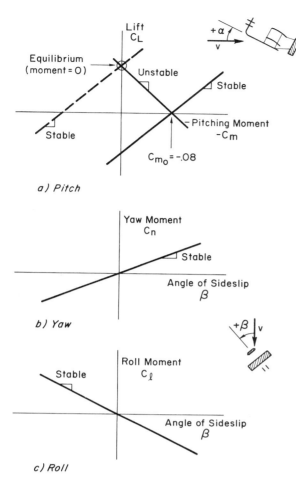

a) Pitch

b) Yaw

c) Roll

4. The three basic moment curves.

a pitching moment tending to rotate the nose down is defined to be negative. The preceding reasoning shows that for stability of equilibrium, the pitching moment must *decrease* when the lift *increases*. This behavior is sketched in the upper portion of Figure 4. The lift is plotted versus the pitching moment, with negative pitching moments to the right of the vertical axis.[4] For stable equilibrium the pitching moment curve, shown dashed in the sketch, must slope from the lower left to upper right and intersect the lift axis; at that point, the pitching moment is zero and small displacements along the curve are accompanied by changes of the pitching moment tending to restore the equilibrium state.

The solid curve labeled unstable also passes through the equilibrium point, but small displacements cause changes of pitching moment which act to increase the displacement. The curve has been drawn to pass through a point labeled—.08, which we shall see later is the value of the pitching moment for zero lift of the 1903 Flyer. The original Flyer was very unstable in pitch. Note that a stable pitching moment curve can obviously be drawn through an equilibrium point

(zero moment) requiring negative lift.

We can apply similar reasoning to motions in yaw, with the result sketched in the middle of Figure 4. If the nose of the aircraft is disturbed to the left of the path, the wind strikes the right side and the aircraft is slipping to the right; this is by definition a positive angle of sideslip. For directional stability, a positive (nose to the right) yaw moment must be generated, causing the nose to swing to the right into the wind. Hence the curve of yaw moment versus angle of sideslip must slope up to the right for stability. Directional stability is provided mainly by the vertical tail; the 1903 Flyer had acceptable, though not large, directional stability.

Finally we consider stability in roll, commonly called "dihedral" effect. The main idea is that if a wing drops, a rolling moment will eventually be generated to restore the wing's level. If, for example, the right wing drops, gravity causes the aircraft to fall to the right, producing a positive angle of sideslip. This motion must then create a negative rolling moment lifting the right wing. If the dihedral effect is positive, the curve of roll moment versus angle of sideslip must therefore slope downward to the right as sketched in the lower portion of Figure 4. Positive or upward dihedral angle of the wings produces positive dihedral effect. Thus, the opposite condition, negative dihedral effect, is sometimes called "anhedral" effect. This was used by the Wrights in their 1903 Flyer.

To summarize, flight in stable equilibrium requires that six conditions be satisfied. For equilibrium, the three moments about the pitch, roll, and yaw axes must vanish. For the equilibrium to be stable, changes of the moments produced by small deviations from the equilibrium state must act to restore the initial state. Application of this requirement has shown what slopes the moment curves must have for a stable aircraft.

In this general context we have treated equally the rotational motions about the three axes. Motions in pitch hold a special position, however, owing to fundamental characteristics of the usual aircraft having a longitudinal plane of symmetry. In steady level flight, the plane of symmetry is vertical and contains both the direction of flight and of gravity. The pitch axis is perpendicular to the plane of symmetry and rotations in pitch directly affect the vertical motion. A fundamental and general property of the pitch stability of aircraft must be emphasized. It is always true that moving the center of gravity forward will make an airplane more stable, for the following reason. When an airplane is in flight, application of an aerodynamic moment, whether by action of the controls or due to an atmospheric disturbance, causes rotation about an axis passing through the center of gravity. Consider the case of a vertical gust, which causes the angle of incidence to increase, so the lift is increased. Imagine that the center of gravity is very far forward, ahead of all lifting surfaces. Then clearly an increase of the lift forces on the wing and tail produce a rotation forcing the nose down, tending to decrease the angle of incidence. This is a stable response. Similarly, if the center of gravity is aft of all lifting surfaces, an increase of angle of incidence will be further encouraged, the change of lift forces causing the airplane to pitch up. This is an unstable reaction. It is reasonable to expect that somewhere between the unrealistically extreme locations there should be a position of the center of gravity for which the aerodynamic forces generate no net pitching moment in response to a distrubance of the angle of incidence. That location of the center of gravity is called the neutral point (NP)—every airplane has one. For a conventional airplane, the neutral point is somewhere on the wing chord, perhaps 30 percent–40 percent aft of the leading edge. For a canard configuration the neutral point is much closer to the leading edge, and often lies ahead of the wing. Positions of the neutral points are labeled NP in Figure 5(a–b).

a) Stable (c.g. ahead of neutral point)

- Center of gravity forward
- Forward surface stalls first → pitch down
- Recovery: "automatic"; control with <u>aft</u> surface (unstalled)

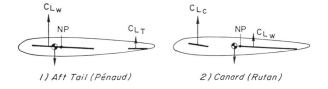

1) Aft Tail (Pénaud)   *2) Canard (Rutan)*

b) Unstable (c.g. behind neutral point)

- Center of gravity aft
- Aft surface stalls first → pitch up
- Recovery: control with forward surface (unstalled)

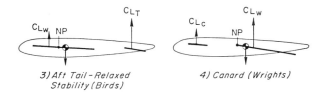

3) Aft Tail - Relaxed   *4) Canard (Wrights)*
Stability (Birds)

5. Stable and unstable wing/tail configurations.

Longitudinal Stability of Aft Tail and Canard Configuration

In his classic paper describing his rubber-band-powered model airplane (Reference 8), Pénaud gave the first detailed analysis of longitudinal or pitch stability. It was not a general discussion; the main purpose had been to show how an aft tail can stabilize pitch motions. The limited scope seems subsequently to have helped create some misunderstanding. For example, it has often not been appreciated that just as a configuration with aft tail is not necessarily stable, so also a canard configuration (which Pénaud did not consider) may be stable or unstable. A correct theory of the stability of all cases did not appear until 1904 in the seminal paper by Bryan and Williams (Reference 9).

A wing alone can be made stable, but only if particular care is taken to use a proper airfoil shape having a reflexed camber line. This seems to have been realized first by Turnbull in 1906 (Reference 10). However, a flying wing brings its own problems and we need consider here only the more common case of a main wing and a smaller horizontal surface for stabilization and control. Four cases are possible: the smaller surface is either forward of aft of the wing, and each of those configurations may be stable or unstable.

The four are shown in Figure 5, with labels citing the best-known examples of each. The lengths of the arrows in Figure 5 represent the relative loads per unit area or lift coefficient; C_l, when the configuration is trimmed for equilibrium in pitch. This shows the most important distinction between stable and unstable configurations. Whatever the relative sizes of the surfaces, the forward surface carries more load per unit area when the configuration is stable: the value of its lift coefficient is greater than that for the aft surface. As a result, if the angle of incidence is increased, the forward surface will usually stall first. This means that for a conventional stable aircraft (Figure 5.1), the wing stalls first and may lose lift suddenly, but the aft tail continues to be effective and can be used to control pitch motions. In particular, the tail can be used to generate a nose-down moment, causing the wing to recover its lift. When the lifting forward surface of a stable canard stalls (Figure 5.2), the nose drops, but while the canard is stalled, precise pitch control is not possible.

An unstable aircraft having an aft tail (Figure 5.3) can be extremely difficult, if not fatally dangerous for man to fly, although soaring birds often fly in this condition. The most critical condition again arises with the behavior at high angles of incidence. Now the aft tail may stall before the wing, control is lost, and the wing stalls soon after. The possibility of operating such configurations successfully, and thereby gaining their advantage of increased efficiency, can be realized with the use of automatic controls. This is a subject of growing interest and application in modern aircraft design.

And so we arrive at the final case, Figure 5.4, the unstable canard used by the Wright brothers (and rarely since!). If the angle of attack is sufficiently high, the aft surface, now the main lifting surface, may stall first. While this appears to be extremely serious, the saving grace is that, unlike the previous case, control is *not* lost. And that is probably why the Wrights were successful with their unstable gliders—they always had control. If the wing has large camber, as with the Wrights' 1903 airfoil, the canard must carry additional lift to balance the large diving pitching moment due to the wing. As a result, the canard may stall first as the angle of attack of the aircraft is increased. That seems to have been the case for the 1903 Flyer as we shall show later.

For our wind tunnel data we estimate that the neutral point of the 1903 Wright Flyer was about 10 percent of chord aft of the leading edge. The center of gravity was 30 percent aft of the leading edge, so the airplane was severely unstable. The difference of those two numbers, −20 percent or −.20 is called the static margin. For current aircraft with automatic control, the greatest negative static margin which is acceptable is about −5 percent.

It follows from the discussion of stability and the neutral point that the slope of the curve lift coefficient versus moment coefficient (or simply lift versus pitching moment) depends on the location of the moment reference point, the position of the center of gravity.

If the center of gravity is moved aft from a stable location, the slope tends to be less upward to the right, becoming more upward to the left. The curve must pass through the value of the residual pitching moment at zero lift, so the moment curves become skewed as shown in Figure 6. Here we have used the data taken with the 1/6 scale model discussed in the following section. The position of the center of gravity for which the curve is vertical is the neutral point; for these data, the neutral point is at approximately 0.10 times the wing chord (c), or 10 percent of the chord.

Vortex Lattice Calculation of Aerodynamics

As a part of the AIAA Wright Flyer Project, two members of the aerodynamics committee have used modern computational techniques to calculate some of the major aerodynamic characteristics of the aricraft. Using two different vortex lattice computer programs, James Howford and Stephen Dwyer of the Douglas Aircraft Company have calculated load distributions, lift and pitching moment for the Flyer. We believe that these are the first such analyses of the aircraft and in fact may be the first applications of vortex lattice theory to a biplane!

The main idea of vortex lattice theory is that the influences of an object in a flow can be calculated by replacing that object by a distribution of vorticity over its surface. Vorticity is an elementary form of fluid motion which can be visualized as a collection of microscopic vortices or whorls—little tornadoes side-by-side. Figure 7 shows how the airplane is treated for this purpose. The wings, canard, and vertical tail are approximated as surfaces having zero thickness,

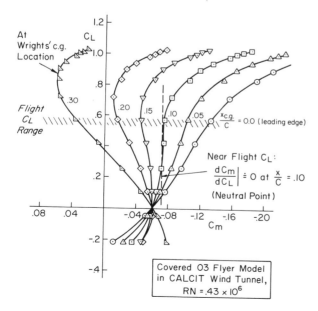

6. Influence of the center of gravity on the pitching moment curve.

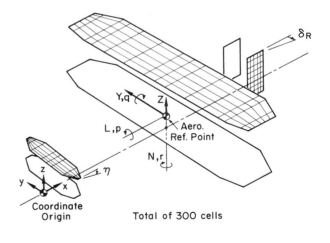

7. Approximation to the Wright Flyer for vortex lattice calculations.

not a bad assumption for the 1903 Flyer. For these calculations the surfaces have been divided into 300 panels, over each of which the vorticity is constant. The procedure requires solving 300 equations for the 300 values of vorticity or loading on the panels. No account is taken of the struts, truss wires, and other structure external to the load-carrying surfaces. In the vortex lattice method the flow is assumed to be inviscid so the drag is zero. The drag due to lift, the induced drag, can be calculated but is not included here.

Examples of Howford's load distributions are given in Figure 8. The loading per foot of span on the lower wing is plotted for several conditions. Figure 8(a–c) shows the influence of canard deflection. In part (a) the load distribution has the nearly elliptical form expected for changes of incidence for the wing alone. Deflection of the canard (nose up) produces downwash behind the canard and upwash in the region outside its tips. This produces a negative loading in the central portion of the wing, and a slight increase in the outboard regions, part (b). The net loading on the wing for changes of both canard and wing incidence is shown in part (c).

In part (d) and (e) of Figure 8 the incremental loadings on the wing due to pitch and yaw rates are illustrated. The wake of the canard has a large influence in pitch, and relatively less in roll.

Not shown here, but evident in the results of the vortex lattice calculations, is the significant upstream influence of the wing. The spanwise loading on the wing produces a strong upwash field decaying within several wing chord lengths. Because the canard is located within the upwash field, this aggravates the contribution of the canard to pitch instability by an additional 25 to 30 percent.

These results show directly the obvious fact that the flow induced by the canard may have substantial effects on the lift generated by the wing, and vice versa. This feature cannot be ignored in analysis of the aerodynamics of the Flyer. Suitable integration of results such as these will give the total lift and moment for the aircraft. The accuracy of the calculations will become apparent upon comparison with data taken in wind tunnel tests.

Results and Interpretation of Wind Tunnel Tests

We have carried out two series of wind tunnel tests within the AIAA Wright Flyer Project. The first used a ⅙ scale model shown in Figure 9. The tests were carried out in the GALCIT ten-foot tunnel at the California Institute of Technology (Reference 11). Because one of the main intentions of the tests was to obtain data for the effectiveness of wing warping, the model was built of wood and fabric, with steel truss wires, very similar to the original aircraft. As a result, the structure was relatively fragile and suffered considerable damage during the test program. Some of the results seem to be biased because of distortions of the wing surfaces.

The second series of tests used the stainless steel model, ⅛ scale, shown in Figure 10 (Reference 12). Extensive tests were carried out, including changes of configuration to investigate possible modifications for the full-scale flying reproduction mentioned earlier. An advantage of the steel model is that data can be taken at higher speeds, or Reynolds numbers. The Reynolds number for the tests ranged from 50 to 90 percent of the value in full-scale flight. In this range the aerodynamic properties suffer only small changes.

Figure 11 is a sketch of the profile of the aircraft showing the definition of several quantities that are important in presenting the data. We have chosen the reference location of the center of gravity to be 30 percent aft of the leading edge of the lower wing and 30 percent of chord above the lower wing. This choice is based on estimates by Professor Hooven of Dartmouth College and by Mr. Charles McPhail of the AIAA Wright Flyer Project. The bottom of the skid rail is the horizontal reference. A line drawn through the centers of the leading edge and the aft spar is parallel to the skid line; this defines the angle of zero incidence of the upstream flow. The same reference

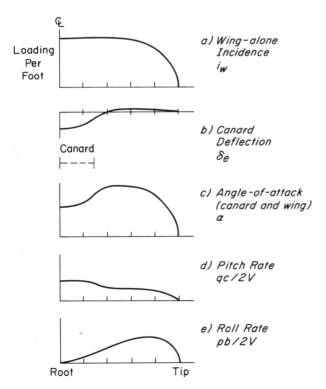

a) Wing-alone Incidence i_w

b) Canard Deflection δ_e

c) Angle-of-attack (canard and wing) α

d) Pitch Rate $qc/2V$

e) Roll Rate $pb/2V$

8. Load distributions calculated with vortex lattice theory.

9. Covered ⅙ scale model in the GALCIT ten-foot tunnel, California Institute of Technology.

10. Stainless steel ⅛ scale model.

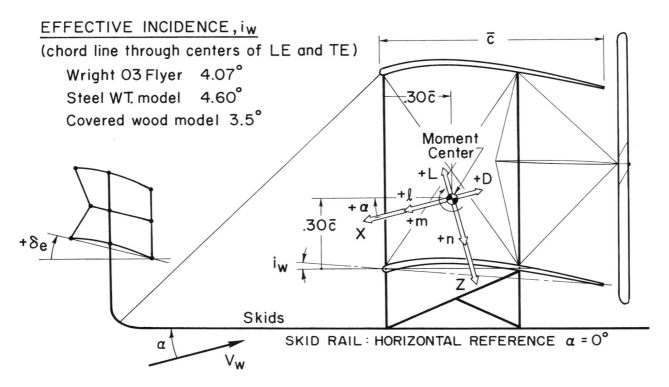

11. Profile of the 1903 Flyer showing reference lines and center of gravity.

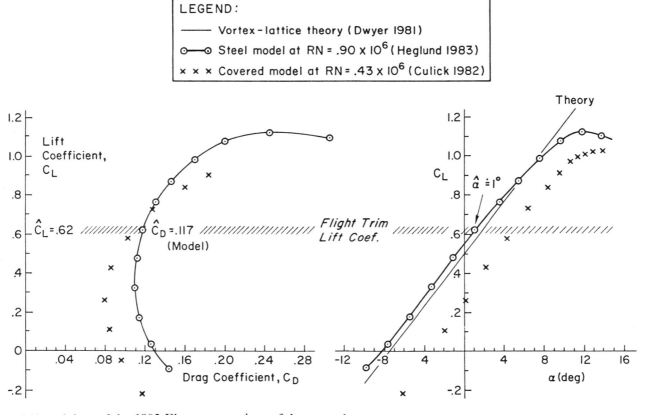

12. Lift and drag of the 1903 Flyer; comparison of theory and tests.

F.E.C. Culick and Henry R. Jex

line defines the zero angle of canard deflection.

Lift and Drag Aerodynamics

Here we shall discuss only a portion of the data, to illustrate some comparisons between experiment and theory, and to cover some of the results used later in calculations of the stability, control, and dynamics of the airplane. Figure 12 shows two of the basic characteristics of an airplane, the drag polar, lift coefficient versus drag coefficient; and the lift curve, lift coefficient versus angle of attack. Because the steel model has larger structural members for strength at the higher test speeds, the drag is larger than that for the ⅙ scale model (called covered model) at the lower lift coefficients. The horizontal crosshatched line is drawn at the value of lift coefficient we estimate to be that for cruising flight of the original Flyer. The agreement of data for the drag of the two models at this value of lift coefficient must be regarded as fortuitous: data for drag are often suspect, and especially for these models the results may be sensitive to the value of the Reynolds number.

The lift curve slope obtained with the steel model is very closely matched by the calculations based on vortex lattice theory, showing an angle of incidence of about one degree at cruise. This suggests again the understanding of aerodynamics possessed by the Wright brothers: it appears that the geometrical setting of the wing, with respect to the skid rail, was very closely that required for cruise flight. The lift curve for the covered model has closely the same slope as the other two results, but is displaced by roughly four degrees to higher angles of attack. This seems to be due to an average reduction of the camber of the airfoil due to distortion of the structure. In any case, both sets of data show that the cruise lift coefficient is well below the value for stall of the aircraft, further evidence of careful design by the Wrights.

Pitching Moment Aerodynamics

A summary of our present understanding of the pitching moment of the 1903 Flyer is given in Figure 13. The best data, those taken with the steel model, are displayed as open symbols; results are shown for three canard settings, 0 degrees and + − 10 degrees. It appears that a deflection of about +6 degrees (nose up) is required for a trim condition having zero pitching moment at the cruise lift coefficient of 0.62. But according to our earlier discussion of Figure 4, this is an unstable condition because the slope of the curve lift coefficient versus moment coefficient is downward to the right.

The data taken with the ⅙ scale covered model are plotted as the crosses. These show a smaller value of pitch down pitching moment at zero lift. Correspondingly, the elevator deflection for trim is nose

down, producing a pitch down moment on the airplane. The smaller pitching moment at zero lift is consistent with the smaller angle of incidence for zero lift shown by the data in Figure 12. Both deficiencies may be explained by somewhat less camber or a small amount of symmetrical twist (trailing edge up) of the wings on the covered model. It appears that the second may be the more likely explanation—unless the data for the steel model and the result of the vortex theory are both in error!

Whatever the case, it is best not to try to "correct" the data, a practice universally understood now, but less well recognized in the Wrights' time. In a letter to Chanute, Wilbur offered the following astute observation concerning Langley's treatment of some of his own data for lift on a flat plate: "If he had followed his observations, his line would probably have been nearer the truth. I have myself sometimes found it difficult to let the lines run where they will, instead of running them where I think they ought to go. My conclusion is that it is safest to follow the observations exactly, and let others do their own correcting if they wish." (Reference 1, p. 171). We follow Wilbur's dictum and present both sets of our wind tunnel data.

The unstable pitching characteristic of the 1903 Flyer is arguably its worst feature, although as we shall see, the lateral characteristics are also poor. The large negative static margin (− 20 percent) meant that the airplane was barely controllable. Three compensating factors made the flights on December 17 possible: the low speed, high damping of the pitching motions, and most importantly the Wrights' flying skills. During their development work leading to the 1905 airplane, the first practical airplane, the brothers

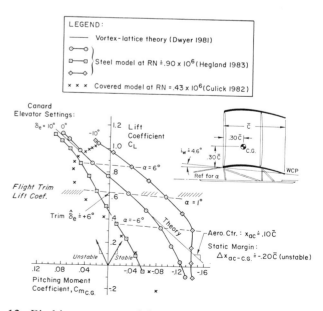

13. Pitching moment of the 1903 Flyer; comparison of theory and tests.

made two important changes: they increased the area of the canard, and they added weight, as much as 70–140 pounds, along the upper longeron to the canard, to bring the center of gravity forward (Reference 13).

Those improvements were made to ease the difficulties they encountered controlling undulations in pitch, a dynamical consequence of the static instability we have been examining. In fact, the most significant cause of the unstable pitch characteristic is the large negative pitching moment at zero lift (see Figure 12). Referring to Figure 4, we see that in order to be able to trim an aircraft for a condition of stable equilibrium, it is necessary that the pitching moment at zero lift be *positive* and at trim lift be *zero*. The Wrights achieved the latter by moving the center of gravity aft, but they could not then satisfy the former.

The large negative pitching moment at zero lift of the 1903 Flyer is due almost entirely to the airfoil. A highly cambered airfoil must operate at a relatively large negative angle of incidence to produce zero lift. At that condition the pressure distribution is such that a large negative (nose down) pitching moment is generated. This is easily demonstrated qualitatively—hold a curved plate in an airstream. It is possible that the Wrights were aware of this behavior, but it is more likely that they were not. Nowhere do they discuss the pitching moment characteristics of airfoils. We have already remarked that they were apparently unaware of the necessity for using the dynamic equations for moments to obtain a thorough and correct understanding of stability.

So the Wrights followed Lilienthal and used thin, highly cambererd airfoils resembling the cross-sections of birds' wings. They were misled to believe that airfoils of that sort produced the highest ratio of lift/drag. There is in fact much truth in this conclusion if data are taken from small wings at the low speeds the Wrights used in their wind tunnel tests. Thicker airfoils having less camber are superior for full-scale aircraft. However, it is the large negative pitching moment of the Wrights' airfoil that is the main issue. Simply by reducing the camber, they could have achieved enormous improvement in the longitudinal flying characteristics of their aircraft. In their later aircraft they apparently reduced the camber, but not as much as they could have.

Directional Aerodynamics

The data for lateral and directional characteristics of the two models, plotted in Figures 14 and 15, seem to agree acceptably well. Note that the scales on the axes are different (the tests were done and the original reports were prepared in two different laboratories). The sideforce generated in sideslip, Figures 14a and 15a, is relatively small because there is practically no

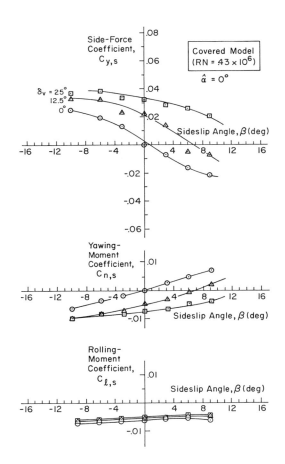

14. Data for lateral and directional characteristics of the 1903 Flyer at trim (⅛ scale model).

side area other than the vertical tail. The slope of the curve C_n versus β is small but positive as it should be for directional stability (Figures 14b and 15b). According to the shift of the curves—i.e., the change of yaw moment with rudder deflection, δ_R—the rudder had plenty of trim control effectiveness. A rudder deflection of ten degrees gives zero yaw moment for a trim angle of sideslip equal to eight degrees. That means that in steady flight, 0.8 degrees of sideslip can be maintained for each degree of rudder deflection. Compare this with a pure vertical tail alone for which one degree of rotation would trim at exactly one degree of sideslip.

Lateral Aerodynamics Anhedral

One of the distinctive features of the 1903 Flyer is that the wings are rigged for anhedral—the tips are "arched" as the Wrights called it, about eleven inches below the centerline. This produces a positive variation of roll moment with sideslip which, according to our remarks in connection with Figure 4c, is an unstable response. Suppose that in steady level flight the right wing tip drops. Gravity causes the airplane

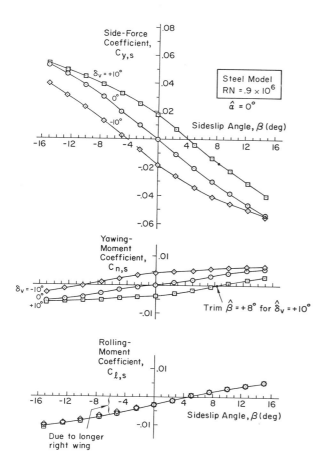

15. Data for lateral and directional characteristics of the 1903 Flyer at trim (⅙ scale model).

to slip to the right, giving a positive angle of sideslip. It is evident that with anhedral, the crosswind tends to strike the upper surface of the lowered wing, forcing it to fall further. This is an unstable response.

Thus we see in both Figures 14c and 15c that the slope of the data for roll moment versus sideslip is positive as expected. The slope is less for the data taken with the ⅙ scale covered model, a result which may be at least partly explained by symmetric twist which would tend to reduce the anhedral of the aft portions of the wing. Both curves are biased so that there is a non-zero (negative) value of roll moment even with no sideslip. This is due to the fact that the right wing has slightly larger span than the left, approximately four inches for the full-scale Flyer. The Wrights built in this small asymmetry to compensate the weight of the engine, which was heavier than the pilot located on the other side of center.

The use of dihedral was invented by Cayley sometime after 1800. Its purpose is to provide stability in roll as described earlier. From the beginning of their work, the Wrights chose not to use dihedral. Writing to Chanute in February 1902, Wilbur refers to a letter by a third party:

> He seems surprised that our machine had a safe degree of lateral equilibrium without using the dihedral angle. He has not noticed that gliding experimenters are unanimous in discarding that method of obtaining lateral stability in natural wind experiments. (Reference 1, p. 217).

While others, like Lilienthal, were shifting their weight to maintain lateral equilibrium, the Wrights were using wing warping, which gave them a great deal more control.

In 1900 and 1901 the Wrights' gliders had anhedral, to discourage the natural tendency for the aircraft to maintain equilibrium, and to allow more effective use of the warp control. Their first glider in 1902 was rigged so the wings were straight (Reference 1, p. 322). But early in their 1902 flying season, the Wrights again installed anhedral. The reason was a problem they encountered because they were gliding close to the surface of sloping ground. Orville wrote in his diary in September 1902:

> After altering the truss wires so as to give an arch to the surfaces, making the ends four inches lower than the center, and the angle at the tips greater than that at the center, we took the machine out, ready for experiment . . . . We found that the trouble experienced heretofore with a crosswind turning up the wing it first struck had been overcome and the trials would seem to indicate that with an arch to the surfaces laterally, the opposite effect was attained. (Reference 1, p. 258).

What they disliked was the obvious consequence of dihedral: if the airplane is exposed, say to a crosswind from the right (which is the same as positive sideslip), the roll moment which is generated by positive dihedral lifts the right wing, as the wind "catches" the under surface. When the aircraft has low directional stability—as was the case for their glider—there is only a weak tendency for the nose to turn into the wind. The net effect for their early gliders was that the left wing tip was driven towards the ground. In an attempt to counteract this motion, Wilbur had operated the canard to raise the nose and the glider stalled, ending in a crash landing. That is the "trouble experienced" mentioned in the above quotation, and the reason why the Wrights favored anhedral which produces the opposite effect: in response to a gust the airplane automatically rolls away from the hill.

That was fine for short, nearly straight flights in gliders at the Kill Devil Hill. The powered flights in 1903 were too brief to show otherwise. But the Wrights discovered during their flight tests of 1904 and 1905 that anhedral has serious undesirable consequences, particularly in turning flight.

Suppose the right wing drops, so gravity causes the aircraft to skip to the right. If the wing has anhedral, this positive sideslip generates a rolling moment tending to lower the right wing further (the crosswind produces increased pressure on the upper surface of the right wing). That is obviously an unstable sequence of events. If, as usually is the case, the aircraft has positive directional stability, the nose will be swung into the wind, here to the right. The net result is that in a right turn, the right wing continues to drop; the aircraft changes heading to the right and what begins as a small disturbance develops into an unstable spiral.

The motion just described is an unstable form of a fundamental motion called the spiral mode. It is part of aircraft dynamic stability, a subject more complicated than the matters of static stability we have discussed so far. For example, an aircraft may be stable in roll (positive dihedral effect), but if the directional stability is sufficiently large, the spiral mode will be unstable. Thus, although the aircraft is statically *stable* in the sense shown in Figure 4, it is dynamically *unstable*. That is, in fact, commonly true of full-scale aircraft.

We shall discuss the dynamics of the 1903 Flyer in the following section using modern techniques of analysis. The Wrights learned the hard way, by flight tests, that anhedral aggravated the spiral instability with dangerous consequences when they tried to turn the aircraft. Although we are here concerned mainly with the 1903 Flyer, it is interesting to learn what the Wrights did about anhedral in their later aircraft. In September 1904 they began practicing turns, attempting a full circle first on September 15. They succeeded on September 20. Then on September 26, Wilbur noted in his diary that Orville had been "unable to stop turning." The same entry appears on October

15, but this time the aircraft suffered serious damage. "Unable to stop turning and broke engine and skids and both screws, Chanute present." On the same day, Chanute noted in a memorandum, "Wright thinks machine arched too much as speed too great across the wind." Thus they seem to have correctly located the problem as the anhedral causing the spiral mode to be so unstable as to make controlled turning extremely difficult.

After removing the anhedral, the Wrights began flying on October 26. The first flight again ended with damage to the aircraft. Referring to this incident in a letter to Chanute on November 15, Wilbur noted "that changes made to remedy the trouble which caused Orville's misfortune gave the machine an unfamiliar feeling, and before I had gone far I ran it into the ground and damaged it again. On November 2nd we circled the field again, and repeated it on the 3rd. On the 9th we went out to celebrate Roosevelt's election by a long flight and went around four times in 5 minutes 4 seconds." Photographs of the airplane with anhedral (August 13) and without anhedral (November 10) are reproduced here as Figures 16 and 17.[5]

Although they were able to turn, success was intermittent. In fact, the day after he wrote to Chanute, Wilbur remarks in his diary, "Unable to stop turning." Their last flight in 1904 was on December 7 and the problem of turning was still unsolved.

The difficulties the Wrights encountered in turns were only partly due to the spiral instability. They believed later (Reference 1, footnote, pp. 469–71) that the control system was a serious cause as well. In all of the flights referred to above, the wing warping and rudder deflection were interconnected as in the

16. Wright airplane, 13 August 1904, showing wing rigged with anhedral. (From *The Papers of Wilbur and Orville Wright*, Marvin W. McFarland, editor, New York, 1953)

F.E.C. Culick and Henry R. Jex

17. Wright airplane, 16 November 1904, showing wing rigged without anhedral. (From *The Papers of Wilbur and Orville Wright*, Marvin W. McFarland, editor, New York, 1953)

1903 Flyer. They recognized that this restricted the control they had and finally in 1905 decided to operate the control independently.

At the beginning of the tests in 1905 (late August) the wings were rigged with a small amount of anhedral which was later removed. Together with independent control of yaw and roll, this gave the Wrights an airplane they could turn controllably at speed and altitude. They then discovered the last problem they had to solve to have a practical airplane: stalling in a turn. Between September 28 when they first flew in 1905 with independent warp and rudder, and October 5 when they flew for 38 minutes, the Wrights learned how to recover from a stall. Wilbur's description in his summary of the experiments in 1905 (Reference 1, pp. 519–21) is a superb statement of the problem and its solution:

> The trouble was really due to the fact that in circling, the machine has to carry the load resulting from centrifugal force, in addition to its own weight, since the actual pressure that the air must sustain is that due to the resultant of the two forces . . . When we had discovered the real nature of the trouble, and knew that it could always be remedied by tilting the machine forward a little, so that its flying speed would be restored, we felt that we were ready to place flying machines on the market.

What a magnificent achievement! In the seven days from September 28 to October 5, 1905, the Wright brothers solved their last serious problem and had a practical airplane. They didn't fly again until 1908, but that's a different part of the story.

Lateral Aerodynamics: Warping Effectiveness

One of the major purposes of the wind tunnel tests with the $\frac{1}{6}$ scale covered model was to investigate the quantitative aspects of wing warping. This method of lateral control was original with the Wrights and after their first flights in 1908 it was quite widely adopted.[6] But within five years it had been almost entirely discarded in favor of ailerons. Hence no wind tunnel data had been taken for the performance of warping. It is an important matter of historical documentation to establish quantitatively how this method of control worked. Some of the results of the GALCIT tests are summarized in Figure 18.

The top portion of Figure 18 shows the effects of warping the wing with no rudder deflection. Data are plotted for no warp (open circles) and maximum warp (open triangles). As noted earlier in connection with Figures 14 and 15, a non-zero roll moment exists with no warp deflection because the starboard wing is longer than the port wing. The roll moment produced is slightly dependent on α, the angle of attack. However, the adverse yaw moment accompanying the warp is strongly dependent upon α. It is adverse yaw in the sense that a right turn produces a yaw moment tending to turn the nose to the left.

Wilbur made his fundamental discovery of adverse yaw during his flights in 1901. He noted in his diary on August 15, "Upturned wing seems to fall behind, but at first rises." Then in a letter to Chanute on August 11, he wrote, "The last week was without very great results though we proved that our machine does not turn (i.e., circle) toward the lowest wing under all circumstances, a very unlooked for result and one which completely upsets our theories as the causes which produce the turning to right or left." These are the first observations of adverse yaw. They could only be made by someone who understood something of aerodynamics and flight mechanics but

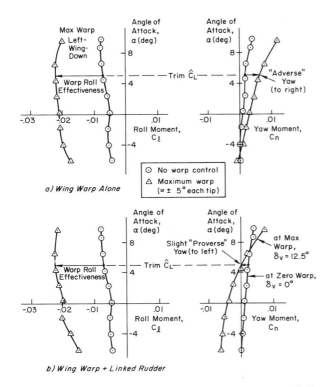

a) Wing Warp Alone

b) Wing Warp + Linked Rudder

18. Data for the lateral effectiveness (⅙ scale model).

especially was trying to learn to fly and was a keen observer.

Adverse yaw arises in the following way. In order to turn, as the Wrights understood from the beginning of their work, it is necessary to generate a component of force towards the center of the turn. This is best accomplished by tilting the lift force on the wing, which is done by banking the entire aircraft. A bank is produced by applying a roll moment, generated by increasing the lift on one wing and reducing the lift on the other. When that happens, whether by wing warping or by using ailerons, the drag is increased on the wing carrying more lift and reduced on the other. The differential drag acts as a yaw moment tending to swing the nose of the aircraft in the direction opposite to that of the desired turn—hence the name adverse yaw. It inevitably accompanies any turning maneuver. Although adverse yaw is low at higher flight speeds, and can be reduced with clever design of the lateral control system, what is really required is control in yaw, and that is why a vertical control surface or rudder must be installed.

The most fundamental aspect of the Wrights' invention of the airplane was the idea of the need for control of both roll and yaw motions. It is the foundation of their basic patent submitted in 1903 and granted in 1906. Wilbur had discovered the problem of adverse yaw in 1901. Their first glider in

1902 had a fixed vertical tail which, with anhedral, gave flying characteristics which they considered to be the most difficult of all their aircraft. They quickly installed a moveable tail which of course gave them the necessary control in yaw.

Warp and rudder deflections were interconnected in the 1902 glider and in the 1903 airplane. Although the controls were later made independent, interconnection was a fortunate choice for the 1903 machine, as we shall see in the following section. The data plotted in the lower portion of Figure 18 shows how simultaneous deflection of the rudder with warping compensates for adverse yaw. The curve labeled δ_r = 12.5° crosses the axis, indicating zero yaw moment, at δ_r = 4°. For the covered model (see Figure 12) this is nearly the angle of attack for the cruise condition. Thus for this speed only, this combination of warp and rudder deflection will produce a roll moment with no adverse yaw, which allows entry to a banked turn with no sideslip—i.e., a more coordinated turn.[7] By disconnecting the warp and rudder controls in their 1905 airplane, and installing both controls on a single stick, the Wrights were then able to execute coordinated turns over a range of airspeeds, in a convenient fashion.

Summary of Wind Tunnel Tests of the 1903 Flyer

The results of these wind tunnel tests have greatly increased our understanding of the flying characteristics of the 1903 Flyer. It appears that the data are reasonable and agree well with predictions based on modern aerodynamic theory.

According to these data, the trimmed flight condition of the aircraft is near the optimum, being at a value of lift coefficient slightly less than that for maximum lift/drag ratio. This provided ample margin below stall of the aircraft, a primary consideration particularly in view of Lilienthal's fatal crash.

The canard gave sufficient power in pitch to control the unstable motions, and the vertical tail was adequate to contol yaw. The combination of wing warp for roll control and a link to remove the associated adverse yaw provided powerful lateral control for banking the airplane and for coping with gusts. No contemporary aircraft had control even approximating that of the 1903 Flyer until after the Wrights publicly flew their improved airplane in 1908.

Dynamical Stability and Control

Our discussion of the wind tunnel data has verified and clarified most of the important static characteristics of the 1903 Flyer—static stability and control effectiveness. With our data, and estimates of a few quantities, we are able to describe quite accurately the dynamics of the airplane, in quantitative terms

34

not available to the Wrights.

Because the Flyer logged a total flight time of only 1 minute 58 seconds, the flight characteristics and handling qualities of the airplane were never fully tested. That it was flyable was of course demonstrated—under severely gusty conditions. In this section we try to convey some idea of how the airplane probably behaved, by examining two elementary transient motions of pitching and turning.

First a few general remarks on unsteady or dynamical motions of aircraft. We assume that the airplane has a plane of symmetry containing the longitudinal and vertical axes.[8] It is then a general theoretical consequence of the equations of motion that if the disturbances away from steady flight are not too large, then the unsteady motions can be split into two parts: purely longitudinal motions involve changes of the forward speed, pitch attitude, and vertical speed, or angle of attack. The lateral motions are out of the plane of symmetry, comprising roll, yaw, and sideways translational motion or sideslip.

The practical consequence of this general splitting or uncoupling of the motions is that, for example, movement of the pitch control (elevator or canard), or a purely vertical gust, will not generate lateral motions out of the plane of symmetry, and conversely. This is the reason why we can rigorously treat the pitch dynamics separately from the lateral dynamics. It is a good approximation to actual motions.

Dynamics of Pitching Motions

We have already established that the Wright Flyer was statically unstable in pitch. That means that if it is even slightly disturbed from a condition of steady flight, there is no tendency to restore the initial steady motion. Thus if the pilot does nothing, the airplane will exhibit a divergent nose-up or nose-down departure.

Figure 19 shows the results of a calculation. Suppose that in level cruise flight[9] the pilot suddenly deflects the canard nose-up one degree and immediately returns it to its previous setting. The same input can be imaged due to an infinitesimally short vertical gust having speed roughly ¾ foot per second, a mild gust. This pulse input is represented in Figure 19a. The remaining four parts of the figure clearly show the subsequent divergent motions in angle of attack, pitch (nose up), airspeed (decreasing), and altitude (increasing). In approximately one-half second the amplitude of the motion doubles. Thus, if the angle of pitch is, say five degrees at some time after the canard has been pulsed, then the pitch angle is already ten degrees only one-half second later.

The airplane alone is obviously very unstable both statically and dynamically. However, it can be controlled by a skilled pilot—the practical consequence

is that the combination of airplane plus pilot is a dynamically stable system. It is entirely analogous to the manner in which a statically unstable bicycle with a trained rider is stabilized. So far as reaction time is concerned, stabilizing the 1903 Flyer is roughly equivalent to balancing a yardstick vertically on one's finger!

Practice is required—the Wrights had lots of that. Here, to demonstrate the idea, we assume that in response to a disturbance the pilot tries to maintain level flight with a simple strategy. The pilot can see the horizon and he knows where some horizontal reference line on the canard should lie with respect

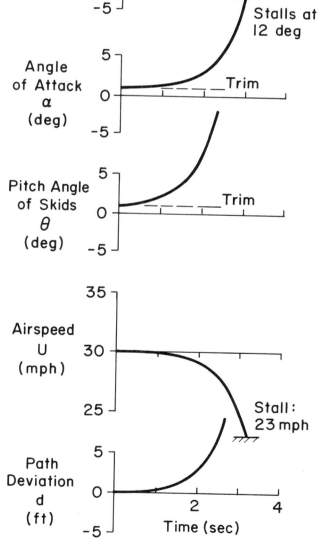

19. Open loop time response in pitch; one degree pulsed canard deflection.

to the horizon in level flight. Then to restore level flight, the pilot deflects the canard by an amount which is proportional to the error between the actual location of the reference line and its desired position in level flight. Thus, the canard deflection is proportional to the pitch error; the constant of proportionality is called the pilot's "gain."

The airplane and pilot, with the assumed proportional control, constitute a feedback system. We interpret its behavior in a root locus diagram, sketched in Figure 20. It is not appropriate here to discuss the theory of this diagram; we shall only explain briefly its meaning and the implications of the results.

Return to Figure 19, at the top, the feedback system comprising the airframe plus pilot is represented as a block diagram. The equation labeled "open loop" is used to calculate the response of pitch angle, θ, to a sinusoidal variation of canard deflection with maximum excursion $+\delta_c$ (nose up) and $-\delta_c$ (nose down). With suitable operations, this formula can be extended to compute the response in pitch to any variation of canard deflection; that is how the

results shown in Figure 19 were found. These results follow from the complete linearized equations for longitudinal motions; their derivations will not be described here. Reference 14 contains a thorough coverage of the theory. The paper by Professor Hooven in this collection shows how to compute the real-time response using a digital computer as a simulator.

The denominator of the open loop response is shown as the product of three factors, one labeled "phugoid" and two together identified as "short period." It is helpful in explaining Figure 20 to remark briefly on the origin of these terms.

We have already noted that under quite general conditions, the longitudinal dynamics can rigorously be treated separately from lateral motions. For most aircraft, there are two fundamental modes of longitudinal motion, called the short period and phugoid oscillations. The phugoid was discovered, analyzed, and named in a remarkable work by F.W. Lanchester in the mid 1890s (Reference 15) based on his observations of the flights of model aircraft.[10] This is a

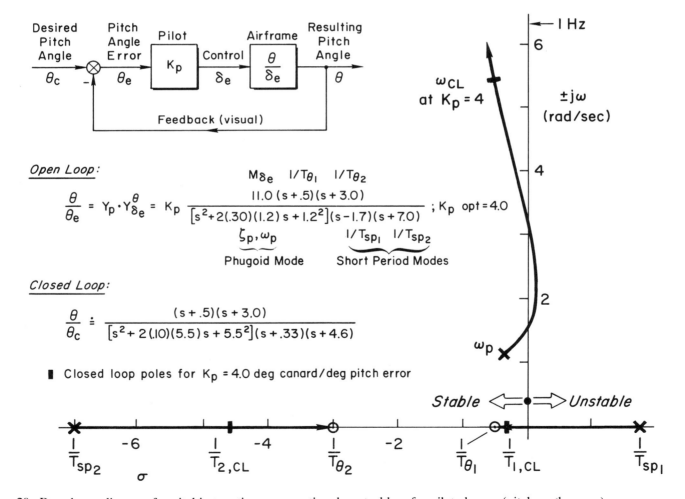

20. Root locus diagram for pitching motions; proportional control law for pilot-closure (pitch angle error).

relatively slow undulating motion whose behavior is dominated by the interchange of kinetic energy of forward motion and potential energy of vertical motion. The angle of incidence remains nearly constant while the pitch angle changes, being horizontal near the maxima and minima of the undulations. It is the phugoid mode which causes difficulties in trimming aircraft when changes of pitch attitude are made.

The second fundamental mode of motion, the short period oscillation, normally has frequency much higher than that of the phugoid mode. Now the aircraft behaves as an oscillator or weathervane in pitch, the mass being the moment of inertia in pitch and the "spring" being proportional to the static stability in pitch, the static margin. The forward speed remains nearly constant and the nose bobs up and down with the angle of incidence approximately equal to the angle of pitch. Because the tail (or canard) also moves up and down with the periodic motions, there is considerable damping of the motion. It is the short period oscillation which usually tends to be most easily excited by sharp gusts and turbulence.

Now back to the 1903 Wright Flyer. In the context of aircraft dynamics, this is distinctly not a conventional machine, which makes its study particularly interesting. First we find that, because the airplane is statically unstable in pitch, the usual short period oscillation doesn't exist. It degenerates to two simpler fundamental motions, one of which decays with time and the other of which diverges following a disturbance. The latter is responsible for the behavior shown in Figure 19. The phugoid is lightly damped, as normally true, and has a period of about six seconds. A typical general aviation aircraft will have a period of say 30–40 seconds for the phugoid and less than 1 second for the short period oscillation. Hence what we call here the "phugoid" is really something between the conventional phugoid and short period oscillation.

The coordinates in Figure 20 are the angular frequency ω in radians plotted vertically, and decay or growth constant, $1/T$ plotted horizontally. The period of motion is $2\pi/\omega$ and the amplitude of motion varies as $\exp(t/T)$. Thus, if $1/T$ is negative—i.e., lies on the left side of the diagram, the motion decays, proportional to $\exp(-t/T)$ and after $t = T$ seconds the amplitude is reduced by a factor of about .37. The crosses in Figure 20 denote the roots of the denominator of the formula for θ/δ_e and represent the natural motions when the pilot does nothing—the canard surface remains fixed. These points are labeled ω_p, denoting phugoid, and $1/T\text{sp}_1$, $1/T\text{sp}_2$, denoting the degenerate short period. Note as remarked above that one of the latter two lies to the right of the vertical axis, representing a divergent motion, and one lies to the left.

Now suppose the pilot acts as described earlier, and continually deflects the canard in opposition to the perceived pitch deviation to maintain a desired pitch attitude—the "loop is closed." The fundamental motions of the complete system, aircraft plus pilot, must clearly be different from those for the "open loop," or aircraft alone. A different formula for θ/δ_e is found and the roots of its denominator are different from those plotted as the crosses. In particular, the values of the roots depend on the gain, K_p, of the pilot—how much he deflects the canard for a unit perceived error. As K_p is changed, each root traces a locus starting at the open loop cross, and hence the name "root locus diagram."

The filled squares in Figure 20 represent the roots when $K_p = 4$, meaning that the pilot deflects the canard by four degrees for every degree of error he sees. Both roots on the horizontal axis now represent stable motions which always decay. The root representing the oscillation has now moved to higher frequency and is still lightly damped. This frequency, roughly 0.9 Hertz, the period being about 1.1 seconds, is in the range for which pilot-induced oscillations will occur. They were likely a problem for the 1903 Flyer, as shown by photographs in which the canard is deflected fully up or down. Motion pictures of the Wright aircraft in 1909 confirm these unstable tendencies.

Figure 21 is a sketch of the time response for a one degree deflection of the canard, corresponding to the

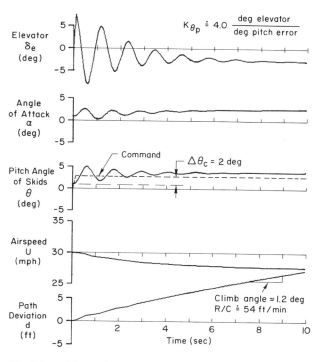

21. Closed loop time response in pitch; one degree pulsed canard deflection.

case shown in Figure 19, but now the pilot exercises proportional control ($K_p = 4$). Both the horizontal speed and the height are successfully maintained constant, but the nose bobs up and down at about 1.1 cycles per second; after about two and one half cycles the amplitude is reduced by half. Thus we have found that even though the airplane alone is seriously unstable in pitch, it is controllable by a reasonably skilled pilot.

This behavior more closely resembles the short period motion than it does the phugoid. As we noted above, the lightly damped oscillation of the airplane alone really cannot be called a phugoid and we have here further support for this view. The origin of this unusual behavior is of course the unorthodox combination of aerodynamic characteristics, including the unstable configuration, and its inertial properties. Having a wingspan of 40 feet, the 1903 Flyer was quite large, but its wing loading was only 1.5 pounds per square foot, which places it in the class we now call ultralights. One important consequence of the low wing loading is that the mass of air which must be moved in accelerated motions—the virtual mass and virtual inertia—is a significant fraction of the mass of the airplane; here about 20 percent. This has been accounted for in the results shown, and explains part of the peculiar behavior.

Approximate values of the virtual inertia have been used in the results given here. The calculations are being refined for a biplane cell having finite aspect ratio. However there is no doubt that the oscillatory motion shown in Figure 21 is real. Films of the Wrights flying their improved aircraft in 1909 show clearly exactly this kind of continuously oscillating pitch control at about the same frequency.

Dynamics of Lateral Motions

The Wright brothers were the first to understand the correct method for turning an airplane. Lilienthal and other glider pilots he inspired were largely content to maintain lateral equilibrium by building wings with dihedral, and shift their weight as required during flight. Contemporary experimenters with early powered aircraft, such as Gabriel Voisin in France, tried to skid around turns by deflecting the rudder. Only the Wrights realized that good roll control is essential for turn entries and exits. They devoted a large part of their flight test program to the problem of turning; only after they were satisfied with their solution did they set out to sell their invention. We have discussed the main features of their system for control of roll and yaw of the 1903 Flyer. Now let us see how it actually performed in flight.

According to discussion in the preceding section, one can treat the lateral motions independently of pitching motions. Before analyzing the particular be-

havior of the Flyer, it is helpful to consider some elementary characteristics of a turning maneuver. Imagine an airplane in steady level flight, and suppose that a means for applying a roll moment is available, by deflection of ailerons, or by wing warping. A fixed value of deflection or warp generates a constant roll moment. If a constant roll moment is suddenly applied, the airplane is first accelerated in roll, but soon settles down to a constant roll rate, so the bank angle increases linearly in time.[11] The rate is constant because the moment due to the distorted wings is compensated by the damping in roll, a moment opposing the movements of the large surface areas normal to themselves. Figure 22 shows this behavior for the 1903 Flyer, the lateral response for an impulsive warp deflection, two degrees of warp held for one-half second, with no rudder deflection. The unstable nature of the motion is clearly shown by the rapid divergence of roll and sideslip angles. Note that owing to adverse yaw, the heading rate is initially in the

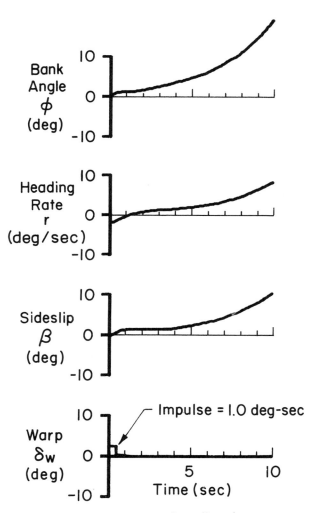

22. Open loop time response for roll angle; ten degrees of wing warp.

direction opposite to that desired.

Evidently, to execute a turn with a fixed bank angle, the roll moment must first be turned on and then removed. Simultaneously, the rudder must be used in such a fashion as to compensate adverse yaw and reduce the sideslip to zero. Considerable practice is required to perform smooth turns.

Analysis of the turn may be carried out using the methods described above. We require that, beginning from steady level flight, the pilot actuate the controls in such a manner as to roll the airplane into a constant angle of bank. The root locus diagram in Figure 23 has been constructed for this situation. Below the block diagram is the equation labeled open loop response, a formula for the response of roll angle to wing warp, δ_ω. The crosses in the diagram again represent the roots of the denominator. One lies to the right of the vertical axis, and corresponds to the

unstable spiral mode described earlier. If the wings are impulsively warped, and returned to their undistorted state, or if the airplane is exposed to a short vertical gust unsymmetrical about the centerline, a divergent spiral motion will develop, as previously explained.

Another root lies far to the left; this is labeled "roll subsidence" and arises from the heavy damping of roll motions. The third root, ω_{DR}, presents a damped oscillation, the subscript DR standing for "Dutch roll."[12] This is primarily an oscillation in yaw angle, a mode due to the action of the vertical tail as a weathervane. This induces oscillatory motions in both roll and sideslip. Damping of the motion is provided mainly by the vertical tail and drag of the wings and struts, due to the differential airspeeds accompanying yaw rates.

These three modes—the spiral mode, the roll subsid-

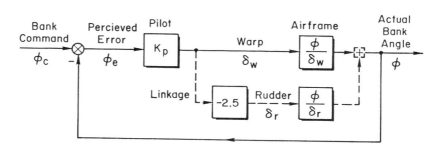

Open Loop (pure warp):

$$\frac{\phi}{\phi_e} = Y_p \cdot Y_{\delta_w}^\theta = K_p \cdot \frac{5.9 \; [.005, 1.3]}{(-3)(3.8)[.6 \, , \, 1.3]}$$
$$\underset{1/T_S \quad 1/T_R \quad \zeta_{DR} \quad \omega_{DR}}{}$$

Open Loop (warp + linked rudder):

$$\frac{\phi}{\phi_e} = K_p \cdot \frac{5.8 \; [.47, 1.2]}{(-3)(3.8)[.6 \, , \, 1.3]}$$

Closed Loop Poles:

	K_p
L	.25
M	.5
⊕	1.0
V	2.0

a) Warp Alone

b) Linked Rudder ($\delta_r = -2.5 \, \delta_w$)

23. Root locus diagram for lateral motions; proportion control law for pilot closure (roll error).

ence, and the Dutch roll—are the natural lateral motions of all aircraft. In this respect, the lateral behavior of the 1903 Flyer is generically the same as conventional aircraft, which normally can be characterized by the same lateral modes. However, the spiral mode is unusually unstable, the amplitude doubling in about 2.5 seconds. This rapid growth is due largely to the anhedral as we discussed earlier. Partly because of the low speed and partly because of the low directional stability compared with the large yaw inertia, the period of the Dutch roll oscillation is relatively long, roughly 4.5 seconds. It is not heavily damped due to the relatively small vertical tail and hence small damping in yaw.

Now consider a simple model of a turn maneuver. Suppose that the pilot wishes to obtain a bank angle equal to ten degrees, which he observes as the angle between the horizon and the canard reference line. As a control law we assume the pilot operates the warp control by an amount proportional to the error,

the difference between the desired bank angle (10 degrees) and that actually observed; the constant of proportionality is the gain, K_p. Two cases are treated: pure warp, with no deflection of the rudder; and interconnected warp/rudder. The second corresponds to the control system in the 1903 Flyer; the drawings obtained from the Smithsonian Institution imply that the rudder is deflected -2.5 degrees for each degree of warp deflection. As for the longitudinal motions, the locus of roots can be calculated for the two cases, shown in Figure 23. For increasing gain, the roots corresponding to the spiral mode and roll subsidence move towards each other on the horizontal axis and then depart vertically, representing the formation of a heavily damped "spiral roll" mode whose dynamics characterize the major portion of the response in roll.

More interesting is the dependence of the Dutch roll "nuisance" oscillation on the gain. For the case of pure warp, this becomes marginally damped for a reasonable value of the gain, one degree of warp for

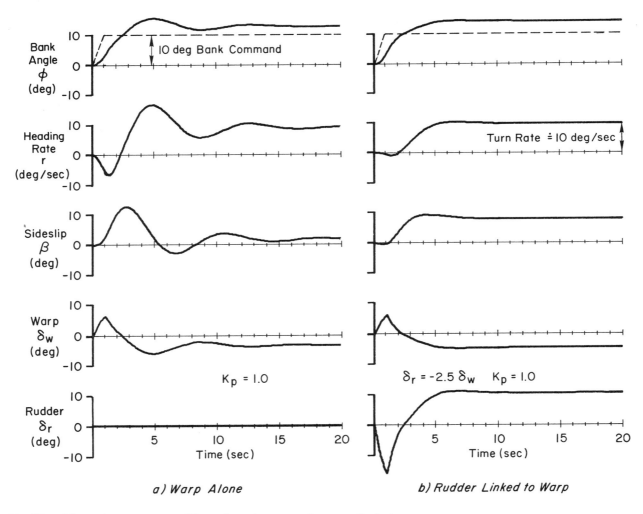

24. Closed loop time response of lateral motions; ten degrees of wing warp.

each degree of perceived error. The time history for this motion is shown in Figure 24a. Large oscillations of both bank angle and sideslip make this a wallowing motion nearly impossible to control and wholly unsatisfactory for practical flying. It is mainly due to the combination of anhedral and uncompensated adverse yaw.

When the rudder deflection is linked to the warping, thereby canceling the adverse law, the result is a turning maneuver which is quite acceptable. The closed loop damping is now much higher—the filled square in Figure 23 lies well to the left of the vertical axis. The much improved response in time appears in Figure 24b. Now the bank angle tends to a constant value, albeit not equal to the desired value (10 degrees) within the time scale shown. There is a fairly large angle of sideslip, so it is a sloppy uncoordinated turn, but surely possible. Thus the interconnection of the warp and rudder is an essential feature of the 1903 Flyer.

As the Wrights discovered in 1905, satisfactory control is achieved only by warp and rudder coordination more complicated than proportional interconnection. It has often been stated, incorrectly, that the Wrights abandoned their interconnected warp and rudder. In their 1908 airplane, with the pilot sitting upright, they put both rudder and warp controls on a single stick. Lateral hand motion caused warp, while fore-and-aft motion deflected the rudder. Consequently any desired proportion of warp and rudder could be produced by operating the stick in a suitable diagonal path. Far from abandoning warp/rudder interconnection, the Wright brothers ingeniously provided a ratio instantly adjustable according to the trim speed or angle of attack. The data discussed earlier (Figure 12) suggest the need for this flexible control.

Further evidence that the Wrights had a most advanced understanding of aircraft control appears in a short French monograph published in 1909 (Reference 16). M. Pol Ravigneaux, evidently instructed by the Wrights, gave a detailed analysis of the stick movements required to accomplish various lateral motions. A few remarks taken from the discussion of his explanation illustrate the point.

> Any movement of the lever L from right to left, or vice versa. . .produces warping which is inverse at the tips of the two lifting surfaces. Any motion of the lever L forward or backward causes. . .a "rotation" of the vertical directional rudder. . .By actuating this lever obliquely, one will obtain *simultaneously* warping and movement of the rudder.

> We know that warping which causes a [left] bank causes simultaneously a [right] turn. . .

> To prepare and make a turn to the left: 1) bank to the left by warping the wings and beginning to turn; 2) straighten out the warped surfaces so as not to continue the banking and smartly turn and rudder to the left. To finish the turn: 3) straighten the rudder;

> 4) level the machine by reversing the previous warp;
> 5) return the wing surface and the rudder to their neutral states.

The author then notes that in practice, the steps describing initiation and completion of a turn overlap, so the use of warp and rudder deflections are executed more continuously to produce smoother turns.

No contemporaries of the Wrights possessed such a thorough appreciation of the details of turn coordination. Our analysis of the dynamics verify the soundness of the Wrights' concepts for lateral control. The results give us even more respect for their ability to accomplish nearly perfect turns.

Concluding Remarks

In 1903, the Wrights understood well the subjects of structures, performance, and control. Their structural design is discussed elsewhere in this collection. Their craftsmanship far exceeded that of their contemporaries. Performance is essentially a matter of balancing forces: weight, lift, drag, and thrust. The theory required is minimal. But it seems clear from analysis of our wind tunnel data, combined with the documented characteristics of their engine and the 1903 airplane, that the Wrights must have paid much attention to this problem. It is not likely accidental that the geometrical incidence of the wing was set at the angle of incidence for cruise flight. Nor was it a matter of luck that the cruise condition gave them a good margin below stall of the wing.

They had learned from Lilienthal that to design a successful airplane they also had to learn to fly. What they added to that lesson was control, unquestionably their greatest contribution. From the beginning of their work they knew that they had to control rolling and not just pitching as their contemporaries had emphasized. Later they discovered that they also had to control yaw motions. That eventually made the 1903 Flyer manageable.

We have used recent wind tunnel data and modern theory of stability and control to confirm the Wrights' unparalleled understanding of aircraft control. Solution of the problem of turning was their supreme achievement in flight dynamics and gave them a marketable airplane. Their success required appreciation of aerodynamics and invention of a simple means for the pilot to exercise lateral control with coordinated wing warping and rudder deflection.

There was much the Wrights did not understand well, mainly subjects which were not clarified until many years later. Perhaps the greatest gap in their knowledge was the theory of rotational motions. Without that they could not formulate precise ideas of stability in contrast to equilibrium.

Their 1903 Flyer was severely unstable statically,

and barely controllable by modern standards of piloting. They detected the most serious difficulties during flight tests in 1904 and 1905, but could correct them only by trial-and-error: they had no guiding theory. For example, they had deliberately used negatively arched wings to combat the tendency for lateral gusts to force them into the hill while gliding. Our analysis of the dynamics has shown that as a result of the negative dihedral, the spiral mode was so strongly unstable as to be marginally controllable. The Wrights spent nearly a year at Huffman Prairie before they removed the negative dihedral in 1904. They had been treating the instability as a problem of lateral control, but it was in fact a problem of lateral dynamics.

The Wrights' emphasis on control unquestionably flowed from their experience with bicycles. They knew that their airplane need not be inherently stable to be flyable. Their creation of the first practical aircraft proved their principles.

The achievements of the Wright brothers appear more remarkable the deeper we understand their technical work. Their own thorough documentation in letters and diaries makes it possible to interpret their work in the context of modern aeronautics. It is astonishing how rarely they strayed from the systematic path to success. What they could not solve with theory and analysis they figured out with careful testing and observations. The standards they set as aeronautical engineers remain unsurpassed.

F.E.C. Culick received his Ph.D. in Aeronautics and Astronautics with a minor in Physics from MIT in 1961. As Professor of Applied Physics in Jet Propulsion at Cal Tech he teaches courses in both fields and currently lectures on Applied Aerodynamics and Flight Mechanics.

Professor Culick is a member of the American Physical Society and the American Institute of Aeronautics and Astronautics. He has published numerous papers and is listed in *Who's Who in America* and *American Men and Women of Science*.

Henry R. Jex is Principal Research Engineer at Systems Technology, Inc., in Hawthorne, California. He holds a B.S. in Aeronautical Engineering from MIT and a M.S. in Aeronautical Engineering from Cal Tech. Since 1953, Mr. Jex's professional experience has been devoted to all aspects of aerodynamic design, flight control integration, and man-machine dynamics, including the conception, development, and testing of aircraft employing minimal flight control systems, tailored airframe characteristics, and novel control surface arrangements. He did the control system design and analysis for the successful Gossamer-Condor and -Albatross human powered aircraft.

Mr. Jex has been an invited lecturer or delegate to several government, academic, or international organizations and has published numerous technical papers and monographs. He is a member of Tau Beta Pi, Gamma Alpha Rho, the American Institute of Aeronautics and Astronautics, Low Speed Aerodynamics Research Association, and the Human Factors Society.

Notes

1. In a letter written on December 22, 1903, Bishop Milton Wright, father of the Wright brothers, referred to their aircraft as the "Flyer" (Reference 1). This seems to be the earliest use of the name. Whether or not Bishop Wright intended to give the aircraft an "official" name is, we suggest, immaterial. He used it, it's a good name, and arguments as to its correctness, in some sense, seem pointless. We subscribe to Gibbs-Smith's usage (Reference 2).

2. It is a remarkable consequence of progress that some of the most advanced aircraft designs are based on unstable configurations, stabilized with automatic flight control systems. These are called "control-configured vehicles." The Wright brothers deserve recognition as the first proponents of this "modern" approach to design. In a further twist of fate, these control-configured vehicles are plagued by many of problems discovered by the Wrights!

3. We must hedge a bit. The right wing of the 1903 Flyer was about four inches longer than the left, to compensate for the weight of the engine, which was mounted to the right of the pilot. This is clear evidence of careful design, and an indication that the Wrights understood some of the need to balance moments as well as forces.

4. This convention is historical and originated with early plots of wind tunnel data prepared in Great Britain. With this convention, the moment curves for stable aircraft fall to the right of the diagram three plots—the drag polar, the lift curve, and the moment curve—could be placed side-by-side on one sheet of paper. Theorists, on the other hand, often do not follow this convention!

5. Plates 84 and 86 of Reference 1.

6. The Wrights used a Pratt truss between the lower wings; the vertical struts carry compressive loads and diagonal wires carry loads in tension. This design provided a rigid, arched "beam" as the forward section of the biplane. The center portion of the biplane was also rigidly trussed at the aft spars. But the outboard 40 percent of the aft spars were trussed by a set of wires to permit controlled warping. When the trailing edges of one pair of tips are twisted up, the trailing edges on the opposite side twist down. Clever structural design is necessary to reduce the wings' resistance to warping so that the control forces are not too large. Those working on the AIAA Wright Flyer project have great respect for the Wrights' ingenious solution to this problem.

7. This conclusion is not wholly correct because our discussion is oversimplified and incomplete. We have ignored the effects of the sideforce generated by rudder deflection.

8. The assumption is only slightly strained because of the deliberate asymmetry mentioned earlier. This has very small effects on the results.

9. Because the airplane is unstable this condition can in reality exist only for a brief time. For calculations we can ignore that practical problem and assume that we start from the desired state of nice level flight.

10. Lanchester chose the term phugoid based on Latin and Greek roots meaning "to fly." He mistakenly selected roots meaning to fly in the sense of to flee—as in "fugitive." Lanchester's aerodynamics was much superior to his etymology.

11. Note that in contrast, for a stable aircraft, fixed deflection of the elevator, which produces a constant

change of the pitching moment, causes a constant change of pitch *angle* (or angle of incidence), *not* a constant pitch *rate*. This is different from roll motion because the pitching moment due to the elevator is compensated by a change in the pitching moment due to the lift of the wing. If the aircraft is unstable in pitch, as the 1903 Flyer was, the two contributions to the pitching moment act together and the pitch attitude of the airplane diverges.

12. The origin of the term "Dutch roll" is obscure. The eminent aeronautical scientist Theodore von Karman once explained that it was a contraction of the naval jargon "Dutchman's roll," alluding to the motion of round-bottomed Dutch ships in the North Sea, or of round-bottomed Dutch sailors ashore. Take your pick.

References

1. McFarland, M., ed. *The Papers of Wilbur and Orville Wright*. New York: McGraw-Hill Book Co., 1953.

2. Gibbs-Smith Charles H. *The Invention of the Aeroplane*. New York: Taplinger Publishing Co., 1965.

3. Wenham, F.H. and J. Browning. Aeronautical Society of Great Britain, Annual Report, 1871.

4. Wells, Albert C. "An Investigation of Wind Pressures upon Surfaces." Thesis. MIT, 1896.

5. Lilienthal, Otto. *Birdflights as the Basis of Aviation*. Translated by A.W. Isenthal. London: Longmans, Green and Co., 1911.

6. Smeaton, John "An Experimental Inquiry Concerning the Natural Powers of Water and Wind to Turn Mills and Other Machines Depending on a Circular Motion." 1752.

7. Langley, Samuel P. *Experiments in Aerodynamics*. Smithsonian Institution Publication 801, 1891.

8. Pénaud, A. "Aeroplane Automoteur; Equilibre Automatique." *L'Aeronaute* Vol. 5. 1872, pp. 2–9.

9. Bryan, G.H., and W.E. Williams. "The Longitudinal Stability of Gliders." *Proc. Roy. Soc. of London*, Vol. 73. 1904, pp. 100–16.

10. Turnbull, W.R. "Researcher on the Forms and Stability of Aeroplanes." *Physical Review*, Vol. 24, No. 3. March 1907, pp. 285–302.

11. Bettes, W.H., and F.E.C. Culick. "Report on Wind Tunnel Tests of a ¹⁄₆—Scale Model of the 1903 Wright Flyer Airplane." Guggenheim Aeronautical Laboratory, California Institute of Technology, GALCIT Report 1034. 1982.

12. "1903 Wright Flyer ⅛ Scale Model Wind Tunnel Aerodynamic Data." 1982.

13. Root, Amos. "My Flying Machine Story." *Gleaning in Bee Culture*. Vol. 33. January 1905. pp. 36–39, 48. Reprinted with title "The First Eye-witness Account of a Powered Airplane Flight (1904)" in *The Aeroplane; An Historical Survey of Its Origins and Development*, by Charles H. Gibbs-Smith. London: Her Majesty's Stationers Office, 1960, pp. 234–39.

14. McRuer, D., I. Ashkenas, and D. Graham. *Aircraft Dynamics and Automatic Control*. Princeton: Princeton University Press, 1973.

15. Lanchester, F.W. *Aerodonetics*. New York: D. Van Nostrand Co., 1909.

16. "Construction et Manoevure de l'aéaeroplane Wright." Monographies d'Aviation No. 5, 1909, Librairie des Sciences d'Aéronautiques (F. Louis Vivien, Libraire-Editeur).

Longitudinal Dynamics of the Wright Brothers' Early Flyers
A Study in Computer Simulation of Flight

FREDERICK J. HOOVEN

Introduction

In 1910 when I was five years old, my father took me in his 1907 Pope-Hartford out to Simms' Station near Dayton, where we lived, to see the Wright brothers fly. It was a good day, with several flights. On one of them I cried out to my father that the airplane was going backward—the little wing was behind the big wing instead of in its regular place in front. My father smiled and said he thought it was a different kind of airplane. I was deeply impressed by the sights and sounds. I can still hear the strange clattering sound of those old engines. When we got home, I found an old orange crate, and put a stick in the ground for a control stick, and I had myself an airplane under the cherry tree in the backyard.

Years later, with a record of those early flights, I learned that only once had the new model B, with its elevator in the rear, ever flown on the same day with its predecessors having the elevator in front.[1] It was the day of the model B's first flight, May 21, 1910. It was also the day of Wilbur's last American flight as pilot, and I may also have seen that.

Ten years later as a schoolboy of 15, still possessed by airplanes, I became the designer of a machine that was being built by a group of schoolmates. Orville Wright was a trustee of our school and it seemed sensible to talk to him about our design. He received us with the same grave courtesy he would have accorded any visiting group, and talked to us in grown-up terms. We were charmed, and went back to see

him many times. He loaned us a little fixture he had made to shape wing sections of wax, and we made wings and tested them in his wind tunnel. He clearly enjoyed our visits and was never too busy to see us, and we loved him. We talked about all kinds of things. He showed us how his desk computer worked in great detail and explained the design of the six-cylinder Wright engine he was shipping to Canada for his boat. He had a wonderful sense of humor and was very sharp witted.

Alone of that group I went back to see him many times during later years and we were good friends until he died in 1948. I often think about Orville Wright and the fun he would have had with a modern computer. I can recall very little that we ever talked about concerning the longitudinal stability of their machines. I do remember his telling that he and Wilbur had flown their first (1900) glider backward down the hill with only sandbags in it, but I missed the entire significance of that remark at the time. When he was talking about the superiority of the RAF15 wing section over the USA4 that we had chosen, he said, "You will have a lot less trouble in controlling it." I didn't understand that either, and I didn't ask him to explain. We talked very little in later years about flying in the old days, and there are hundreds of questions that I now wish I had had the sense to ask him while he was living.

In 1969 I read Charles Gibbs-Smith's *The Invention*

of the Aeroplane (Reference 1). It was the best statement I had seen of the case for the Wrights as undisputed claimants to the honor of being the first to fly in controlled powered flight. It had objective evaluations of their capabilities and those of rival claimants, and I was most favorably impressed. However, it made the first mention I had ever seen of the longitudinal instability of the early Wright machines and criticized the Wrights for persisting with the designs.

I wrote to Gibbs-Smith at once, expressing my appreciation of his work, but taking issue with his statement of instability, sending a small flying model canard to make my point. He replied modestly saying that he was no expert but his expert friends had assured him the machines were indeed unstable.

I couldn't find an accurate technical description of the Wright machines to prove my point, and had no success in trying to persuade any of my qualified friends to undertake a study. It was 1978 before I had finally reached the point of deciding I would have to do that myself. I knew that having read all the books available before 1920 and having taken a few undergraduate courses in aeronautics in the 1920s didn't qualify me for the job, but I decided that I could learn enough to simulate the flight of the old machines on the computer in two dimensions only.

I began with purely linear characteristics, but soon found out that it was possible to get into situations that demanded real-life non-linearity and aerodynamic data. There were not many laboratory tests of Wright airfoils, but I began by using the Wrights' own reports of their wind tunnel work, reported in McFarland's *Papers of Wilbur and Orville Wright* (Reference 2). I found it surprising that the Wrights had made no recorded measurements of center of pressure location until 1905, at the time they had finally decided to increase the size of the stabilizer on their 1905 machine, and finally solve their longitudinal control problems. There was no correlation between the Wrights' wing sections and their center of pressure figures, so I used the center of pressure figures of the Eiffel 10 (Reference 3) without realizing that in combination with the lift coefficients of the Wrights they would give an optimistically low value of pitching moment coefficient. Even so, there was no doubt the machines were unstable, and I made my acknowledgments to Gibbs-Smith both publicly (Reference 4) and personally, but I defended the Wrights against his charge that they were wrong in continuing the unstable designs as long as they did. I argued that they had avoided a much worse risk when they eliminated the possibility of diving after a loss of flying speed.

Being invited to join a group from the Los Angeles Chapter of the AIAA who planned to build a "look alike" flying replica of the 1903 Flyer, plus a historical replica for wind tunnel testing, I resolved to upgrade my obsolete capabilities in aerodynamics and modernize my concepts of longitudinal dynamics. Having no colleagues nearby with similar interests, I welcomed the prospect of people to interact with.

The following discussion gives a brief summary of the Wrights' careers with major attention to their learning and experiences as pilots, and to their canard-type Flyers, with major attention to their longitudinal control and stability characteristics. Its purpose is narrowly confined to the longitudinal dimension only; to the plane of symmetry. Fortunately there is negligible interaction between the logitudinal control of these machines and their lateral or directional controls.

To accomplish a simulation of their flying behavior it has been necessary to establish the aerodynamic characteristics of these machines from basic aerodynamic theory, since there had been up until recently no experimental determination of these characteristics. It has also been necessary to make a careful study of what has been recorded of the flying characteristics of the machines and their pilots. The flights of the 1903 Flyer and the essentially similar 1904 and early version 1905 models, which, because of their inadequate controls were highly dependent on the quality of the piloting, have provided enough information to base a program of pilot simulation. This program is able to reproduce some of the historically recorded flights with sufficient realism to encourage me to believe that they actually reproduce the flight characteristics of the Wright brothers and their Flyers.

I am greatly indebted to Thayer School of Engineering for countless hours on Dartmouth's superb computer system; to E. Eugene Larrabee, who reviewed my early program in detail and made useful and constructive criticisms on it; to my West Coast colleagues, Frederick E. C. Culick, Henry Jex, and Charles McPhail, for useful data, ideas, and comments; to Tom Crouch, Howard Wolko, and Jay Spenser of the NASM staff for assistance in gathering data; to Walter P. Maiersperger for useful criticisms and comments; and to Candace Dubé who processed the copy for this report.

The Wright Glider

The Wrights learned to fly, developed their control concepts, and tested their aerodynamics on their gliders. Their fundamental means of longitudinal and lateral control, the forward stablizer and the warping wing, remained essentially unmodified from the beginning of their experiments throughout the period from 1899 to 1910, but the rudder and its interaction with the lateral control continued to evolve during the entire glider period, 1900 to 1902, and beyond to

1904 when the rudder was given its own separate control.

They built their 1900 glider (Figure 1) according to the aerodynamic tables of Otto Lilienthal so that it could be flown as a man-carrying kite tethered in the wind at Kitty Hawk, and they planned to teach themselves to fly that way. It was a surprise, therefore, when they found that their machine would not support a man in a wind of 16 miles per hour as they had calculated it should. They therefore flew the machine as a kite with sandbags on it, and measured the forces of lift and drag. They flew the machine backward down the hill, finding that it was stable that way, but decided they would stick with their forward stabilizer to avoid being killed in a dive following a stall, as Lilienthal had been. They finally made a few glides, finding out if they rigged their machine with a dihedral angle to gain stability, they lost a certain degree of control and the machine responded to wind gusts. Here was born their distrust of stable machines. It was not until 1905 that they finally tried a slight dihedral angle for improved lateral stability, long after Kitty Hawk's wind had been left behind.

They attributed the lack of lift of the 1900 machine to insufficient camber of the wing section, so the 1901 glider was built with a camber of 1/12 and a much greater wing area. It was almost impossible to control and it disappointed them in having not as good a glide angle as their 1900 machine. They were greatly disappointed with the performance of the glider and discouraged to find that Lilienthal's aerodynamic data were in error, as were his words about center of pressure movement. We are fortunate that E.C. Huffaker, representing Octave Chanute, was a visitor in the Wrights' camp at Kitty Hawk during the early part of the 1901 season in which they were struggling with the problems presented by their 1901 glider.

Huffaker's notes (Reference 5) illuminate the Wrights' thinking on the subject of the stability of their machine. On July 29, 1901, he noted: "The equilibrium is not satisfactory and the Wrights think of making radical changes, placing the rudder in the rear, or possibly rebuilding the machine.[2] The experiments have satisfied all of us that as the angle [of attack] changes the center of pressure moves forward. The curvature of the surfaces while at rest is about 1 in 20. When carrying a [total] weight of about 240 pounds the curvature increases to 1 in 12 and is constantly changing. To render the curvature more constant it is proposed to bring the rear spar forward so as to insure less bending of the ribs under pressure" (Reference 6). (The ribs were thin wooden strips and there was only a single layer of wing covering.) "It has been suggested that it would be well to bring the rear spar forward so far as to cause the rear of the ribs to bend upward under pressure and so lessen the curvature."

That this was in fact done may be seen by looking at Huffaker's sketch, Figure 2, of the 1901 wing

2. Huffaker's sketch, taken from his diary, of the wing section of the 1901 glider before and after camber reduction. Included at top are typical Huffaker flight records.

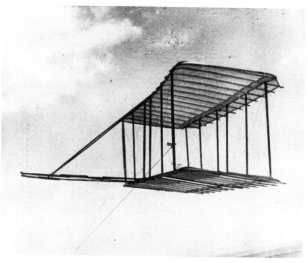

1. The 1900 glider. (From the Collections of the Library of Congress)

3. The 1901 glider. (From the Collections of the Library of Congress)

section before and after the rebuilding operation, in which a third spar was added to push down the rear of the ribs to flatten them out, and then looking at the picture, Figure 3, of the 1901 machine in flight after the modification was made. In the photograph it is clear that the wing ribs are bent up more in the rear in flight than is shown in the sketch. Looking at this rib, with its considerable reflex rear edge, it might be surmised that the machine had actual positive longitudinal stability. That it was indeed so is shown by a note made by Huffaker on August 13, after the modifications were made. "Fourth experiment, 200 feet, angle 9° straight and steady, acting automatically, i.e. leaving the rudder unchanged."

The Wrights didn't like Huffaker: he shirked camp duties, complained about hardships, and didn't change his linen as often as they thought was necessary. But we owe him much for his notes, which were much better than the Wrights kept. Huffaker's note of the "automatic" flight of the glider was not recorded elsewhere, nor was his note of July 29, 1901, that "Orville Wright was on the machine." There is no other record of Orville's flying before 1902.

The end of the 1901 season was a time of truth for Wilbur and Orville Wright. Having found Lilienthal's tables to be mistaken, they realized that they would have to develop their own aerodynamic information if they were to make any further progress in flight, and they were deeply discouraged. Finally, they decided they were committed to flying. It was the turning point in their careers at which they ceased to look on their work as a sport and undertook a serious commitment to proceed through the development of a power-driven machine.

Their 1902 glider was designed from the results of their 1901 wind tunnel experiments, and it was a major advance over anything that had ever been built

before. By far the largest machine ever flown, it had a higher aspect ratio and less wing camber than the original version of their 1901 glider. The Wrights recorded that its wing camber was $\frac{1}{25}$ (Reference 7), but it may be seen from photographs to have been less than that in flight. This machine saw the final development of their ideas of control when its original fixed biplane rudder was replaced with a single-plane rudder that moved in conjunction with the wing warping to counteract the turning effect of the increased drag on the rising side. Its system of wing warping was changed so that only the rear half of the outer section of the wing was moved, as may be seen in Figure 5, instead of twisting the entire biplane structure, as may be seen in Figure 3, of the 1901 machine in flight. They made more than 1,000 glides in this machine and each man had soared in it for over a minute.

Although the Wrights had repudiated the concept of shifting weight for glider control, as had been practiced by their predecessors, there can be no doubt that so long as the operator's weight was greater than that of the glider it was utilized for optimizing the longitudinal control of their machines. As a result of this they were not prepared for the fractious pitching behavior of their first powered machines, which had crucial differences in wing-rib construction, with the first doubled-surface wings, and which were far too heavy to be susceptible to trimming by weight-shifting.

The Early Wright Flyers

The Wrights built five different models of front-stabilizer, or "canard" Flyers, the 1903, 1904, 1905, 1907, and 1909 models. The last was a unique machine built for the special purpose of meeting the Signal

4. The 1902 glider. (From the Collections of the Library of Congress)

5. The 1902 glider banking, showing wing warping. (From the Collections of the Library of Congress)

Frederick J. Hooven

Corps speed requirements, and had no influence on subsequent development, so will not be given further attention here. The remaining four are conveniently divided into two types aerodynamically: the 1903 and 1904 machines which differed only in small respects, and the 1905 and 1907 models which were substantially identical to one another. The only important difference between these two general types concerns the size and operating radius of the stabilizer, which was too small for adequate control in the two earlier models. The wings of the four were substantially identical aerodynamically, differing only in structural details and weight.

The 1905 machine was built similar to the 1903 and 1904 models, but after it was wrecked on its eighth flight, it was rebuilt in the later form. All references to the 1905 machine here are made to the later form.

The brief flying life of the 1903 machine has been adequately recounted many times. It made only the four flights on December 17, 1903, which totaled about 95 seconds, before it was wrecked when the wind rolled it over. That wasn't much, but it was 95 seconds longer than anyone had ever flown before. The pitching tendency of this machine was very troublesome, and at that time it was attributed to the overbalancing of the stabilizer.

The 1903 machine's brief history gives little basis for conclusions about its characteristics, but much can be learned by studying the flight of the 1904 Flyer, which was substantially identical in its specifications, except that it had more power, about 16 horsepower that gradually grew to 18 at the end of the season as the engine became worn in. This machine existed in three phases, the first of which was the same as the 1903, except for about 34 pounds of added weight. The second phase followed the rearward movement of the center of gravity from 29 percent chord to 32 percent. This move was made in the expectation that it would improve the pitching, or "undulation," but it had the reverse effect (Reference 8) and was quickly followed by the third phase when a 70 pound weight was hung on its stabilizer frame, moving the center of gravity forward to 23 percent chord. This reduced responsiveness to the elevator and increased the period of oscillation in pitch, but it did not cure the problem.

The 1905 machine was wrecked in a spectacular crash on its eighth flight on July 14, 1905, which Wilbur described in the following words: ". . . the machine began to undulate somewhat and suddenly turned down at a considerable angle, breaking front skids, front rudder, upper front spar, about a dozen ribs, the lower front spar and one upright. O. W. was thrown violently out through the broken top surface and suffered no injury at all" (Reference 9). On July 25, Wilbur's diary gives their first recorded measure-

6. The 1903 Flyer before its flights. (Courtesy Smithsonian Institution)

7. The famous shot of the first flight, with Orville aboard and Wilbur standing at right. (From the Collections of the Library of Congress)

8. The beginning of the third flight, showing the extreme roll. (From the Collections of the Library of Congress)

ment of center-of-pressure location (Reference 10), and on August 24 the machine took to the air for the first time with its new and larger stabilizer and front structure. Before that date there had been constant trouble with what Wilbur called "the tendency to undulation that has marked our flights with powered machines" (Reference 11). From August 24 onward flying developed rapidly. There was no longer the tendency to undulate and there were far fewer crashes. The year ended with seven flights that totaled nearly three hours duration, more than four times the total accumulated on their powered machines prior to August 24, 1905 (Figure 9).

This sturdy machine was rebuilt in 1908 with two seats, to accommodate two sitting occupants instead of the single prone operator, and with a 30-horsepower engine. It was taken to Kitty Hawk for flights to refresh the Wrights' piloting skills after two and one-half years of nonuse, and to accustom themselves to the new control system necessitated by the seated position. After each man had about 15 minutes on it, it was wrecked. Following this, Wilbur went to France and Orville back to Dayton, each to prepare for his first flight in public before a skeptical audience.

The 1905 Flyer was the first real airplane: built, developed, and flown for more than 39 minutes in a single flight before any other powered airplane had even left the ground in controlled flight. It is still in existence, having been restored in 1948 in a program that got under way before Mr. Wright's death. There should be a flying replica of it.

The 1907 machine was aerodynamically similar to the 1905 machine but somewhat heavier. At least seven of this model were built by the Wrights and it is possible that they were not all exactly alike (Reference 11). It is shown in Figures 10–13. No authentic drawings exist of this machine, but since the first of them was begun at the same time as the 1905, it is assumed that the wings are identical, and that, except for some changes made in the stabilizer actuation, it is aerodynamically identical to the 1905 machine. It is the machine that amazed the world in 1908 in France and in Washington, D.C., when the Wrights flew in public for the first time. It is the machine that crashed in Washington, D.C., killing Lieutenant Selfridge and seriously injuring Orville. In those early days, it established a series of records for altitude and duration, and, before Orville's accident in Washington, the records went back and forth across the Atlantic several times. It is the machine on which the first formal student training was accomplished, with Tissandier, De Lambert, and Lucas-Girardville in France, Calderera and Savoia in Italy, and Englehard in Germany. One of this model is still preserved in the Deutsches Museum in Munich, the only one known to survive, although a second is said to have been recently uncovered in France.

As I have indicated, and will show later, the position

10. The 1907 Flyer, Orville aboard; 1908 Signal Corps tests.

1907/1909 WRIGHT FLYER

11. Drawing of the 1907 Flyer. The draftsman is unknown, but authenticity of details indicates that he must have had access to the machine.

9. The 1905 Flyer over Huffman Farm. (From the Collections of the Library of Congress)

50

Frederick J. Hooven

of the center of gravity of the canard is critical to its stability. It is interesting to note the difference between Orville's machine in Washington and Wilbur's in France in 1908. The two seats of Orville's machine were arranged so that the occupants' legs extended for almost their full length forward of the wing's leading edge (see Figure 12), while Wilbur's machine had the seats so that the knees of the occupants were about even with the leading edge. This difference in occupant position would make a difference (Figure 13) of about 3 percent chord in the position of the center of gravity of the machine. It casts light on Orville's statement to Wilbur in a letter written in 1908, "I had noticed in my flights with Lt. Lahm and Major Squier that there did not seem to be any too much surplus pressure on the under side of the rudder (stabilizer). It seemed, however, to make the flight steadier than when I was on board alone" (Reference 13).

The Wrights have been criticized for persisting as long as they did with their unstable canards, a subject on which there is much misunderstanding and misinformation. The canard is not intrinsically unstable. Its stability depends on center of gravity location just as in any machine, although the range of stability is smaller in the canard. Their avowed reason for the use of the canard was to avoid the dive following a stall, which they recognized as the cause of the death of Otto Lilienthal, their esteemed predecessor, and which remains as the cause of many flying accidents today. They were well aware that the rear stabilizer configuration made it easier to attain stability, and they had flown their 1900 glider backward, loaded with sandbags, to prove it (Reference 14), but they made the deliberate choice of instability. They wanted to have the machine go where they directed it to go,

not where it chose to go, or where the wind might take it. They were riders of bicycles and were not afraid of instability.

The canard arrangement (Reference 15) and its accompanying longitudinal instability in all probability saved the Wrights from serious accident during the period, ending in 1905, when they were learning to avoid the stall. They repeatedly had trouble with stalls in turns, until they realized that turning raised the stall speed and that they must put the nose of their machine down to hold its speed during a turn. They were, therefore, wise to retain that system during 1905. They had quite enough to do to build more machines and prepare for public flying without trying to develop a radically different machine for 1908, which their critics imply that they should have done. The 1907 machine was an almost exact duplicate of the 1905 model, except for its greater weight and higher power.

Before they undertook to place their machines on general sale in 1910 they developed a new, stable machine with the stablizer in the rear, the model B, the first flight of which I witnessed. This machine, ironically, was involved in a number of fatal accidents that resulted from stalling, with the result that the model C soon replaced it, with its center of gravity farther back and with less stability.

Simulated Flight

These simulations are two-dimensional only. They are concerned with motion in a single plane, up and down, forward, and angularly in pitch angle. It is fortuitous that the 1903 flights were all in a straight line. This does not mean that because no attempt was made to turn the airplane that the lateral control

12. The 1907 Flyer, Orville aboard, showing forward seating position.

13. The 1907 Flyer, Wilbur aboard, showing seating position.

was unused. On the contrary, as may be seen from Figure 8 taken just after the start of the third flight, the pilot had more to do than control the plane in pitch.

The aerodynamic specifications of the planes studied have been established as shown in detail in Appendix 2.

Over the years in which simulation programs have been developed, the general flying characteristics of these old machines have shown themselves to be encouragingly independent of specific aerodynamic assumptions and quantities. This has given me a considerable amount of confidence that the simulation does represent the way the machines actually flew. In this section of the report I will present simulated flights under the conditions of December 1903, and flights designed to demonstrate the dynamic stability of the airplane-pilot combination for the various phases of development of the Wright brothers canards. The flights demonstrate some of the historic and unique flying characteristics such as the "undulation" of the 1903 and 1904 Flyers and the much lesser, but unique continuous small-angle pitching motion of the 1907 machine, as recorded on film in the famous motion picture made at Centocelle in 1909 (Reference 45). Finally, these flights demonstrate that the Wright canards did in fact remain nearly level after a stall, which was why the Wrights chose that form in the first place, and why they stuck with it throughout the development of their machines.

Since it is not possible to simulate the flight of an unstable machine without some simulated means of controlling it, I will discuss the problem of simulating the airplane pilot.

The Wright Brothers as Pilots

Wilbur and Orville Wright not only invented the airplane, they also invented the airplane pilot and the very concept of airplane control. Until their widely disseminated publication of 1901 (Reference 16), the airplane was conceived as a craft that, like an airship, would be steered right and left with a rudder, and up and down with a horizontal rudder, by anyone who happened to be aboard, without previously acquired skills. It was what Charles Gibbs-Smith called the "chauffeur mentality," and it was the universal state of mind before the Wrights' published work, and the general view of would-be aviators. Their concept of controllability was not understood or accepted until their public flights in 1908.

Builders and riders of bicycles, the Wrights conceived the airplane from the very first as a craft that, like the bicycle, depended on its rider to maintain its equilibrium. It was therefore perfectly natural for them to assume that in order to achieve powered flight, it would first be necessary not only to develop the airplane, but also to develop its controls and the skills necessary to operate them. From the beginning they assumed that the means of control of their machine would be by movement of its surfaces.

I make no distinction between one Wright brother and the other, not only as pilots but in any of their contributions to flight. The basis exists for comparing their abilities to those of pilots of a later generation. I have known three of the men who received their flight instruction from Orville well enough to have heard their opinions of him as a pilot. They all spoke of him as a superb pilot with lightning-quick reflexes and sure responses. While no such basis for comparison exists where Wilbur is concerned, there can be no doubt he was Orville's equal as a pilot, as may be seen from the records of their flights as they have been recorded by Renstrom (Reference 17).

The Wrights acquired their flying skills on their gliders, and they needed all their skills to control the 1903 machine on the four flights it made on December 17 at Kitty Hawk. They flew into a gusting wind that averaged about 20 miles per hour, two-thirds of the flying speed of their machine. They attributed the difficulties with excessive pitching to the fact that the elevator was overbalanced, but when they built the 1904 machine with the elevator pivot point farther forward, the pitching persisted.

The records revealed that their skills were not quite up to the task of controlling the 1904 machine or its short-lived 1905 successor of similar proportions. In these machines there was a total of 90 recorded actual flights, out of which there were 19 instances of landings with damage to the machine. As nearly as can be judged from the sparse records, 8 of these were the result of pitch-control inadequacies, 6 from lateral control, and 5 of which no clue survives.

Of 37 recorded flights with the remodeled 1905 machine, there were only two that resulted in recorded damage, the third and sixth after the rebuilding. In the last 31 flights there was no further damage, and 23 of these flights racked up more than four times as much flying time as in all the flights of the predecessor models. It was without doubt a help that the 1905 machine had 20 horsepower available and could therefore fly at a somewhat higher speed, 50 feet/second (34 miles per hour) instead of 44 feet/second (30 miles per hour). Its performance was sufficient that the Wrights decided it could be put on sale.

No discussion of the Wrights as pilots is complete without reference to their system of flight controls. Up to the end of 1905 all their flying in glider and Flyer had been made in the prone position, using the hip girdle to actuate the combined wing warping and rudder control, and a left-hand lever with fore-and-aft movement to actuate the elevator. Later in 1905 they separated the rudder from the wing warping and added a right-hand lever with fore-and-aft movement to actuate it.

When they started to fly in a sitting position in 1908 they rebuilt the trusty old 1905 Flyer with a new 30-horsepower engine and two seats on the wing. The controls were new and different, since the hip girdle was no longer used. Instead, a second direction of motion was added to the right-hand lever, which was moved right and left to control the wing warping in addition to moving fore-and-aft to control the rudder.

Each brother got about 15 minutes on that machine, including one trip each with a passenger, the first ever carried, before it was wrecked. Therefore, it was with but 15 minutes of flying experience with the new control system after two and one-half years of not flying at all that Wilbur undertook their first flight in public, in France before a critical and skeptical audience, and Orville shortly after made their first public flight in America. After having made three short flights in France and wrecking the machine on the third landing, Wilbur wrote to Orville, "I haven't yet learned to operate the handles without blunders" (Reference 18).

Wilbur and Orville Wright were the first ever with "the right stuff." They needed every bit of it that summer of 1908.

The Simulated Pilot; Simulating the Wright Brothers

It is meaningless to speak of the dynamic stability of a statically unstable system, and the longitudinal dynamic stability of the Wright canards is evaluated in combination with a simulated pilot, the responses of which are intended to reproduce those of the Wrights as nearly as can be deduced from the historical record.

I began by assuming that any algorithm that reproduced a plausible performance would be satisfactory as a pilot, and for the sake of convenience I chose to use airspeed as the target variable, with a response to angular velocity in addition. This algorithm was:

$$\Delta B = Q2\,(V - Q1) - Q4w$$

in which Q1 is the target airspeed, Q2 was adjustable from .015 to .03 and Q4 from 30 to 60.

There was a reaction-time delay that could be varied from 0 to .08 seconds, of which a typical value

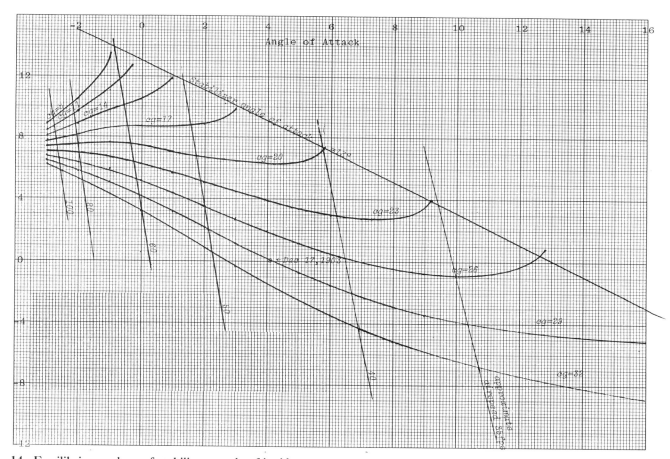

14. Equilibrium values of stabilizer, angle of incidence vs. angle of attack, 1903 Flyer.

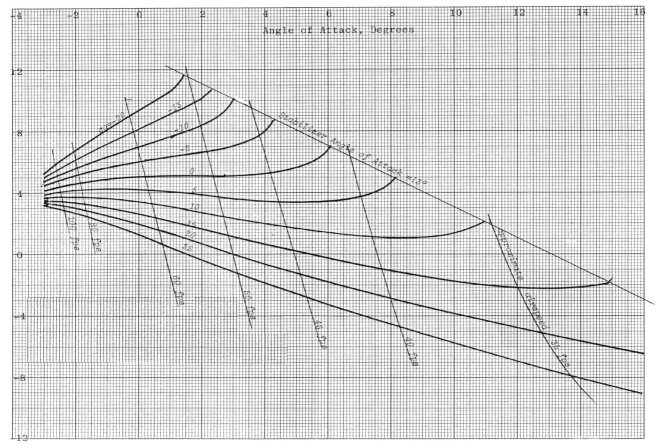

15. Equilibrium values of stabilizer, angle of incidence vs. angle of attack, 1905 Flyer.

was .04.

This controlled the aircraft in a realistic manner, but it was criticized by Eugene Larrabee (Reference 19), who noted that real pilots do not in fact use airspeed as their basic response stimulus, but rather seek to maintain the pitch attitude of their machine relative to the horizon. Acknowledging the fairness of this comment, but also recognizing that the pilot, when faced with irregular air currents or irregular engine output, would be in trouble if he did not also pay attention to his angle of attack, or airspeed, I devised a new algorithm that used the pitch angle of the machine as its target value:

$$\Delta B = Q2 (Q1 - Ap - Ai)$$

But whenever the angle of attack deviates from Q1 by more than 1 degree the pilot responds to angle of attack as well as to pitch angle:

$$\Delta B = Q2(Q1 - Aa/2 - (Ap + Ai)/2)$$

The simulated pilot senses, in addition, angular velocity and angular acceleration only after the angular velocity exceeds $+ - .02$ rad/sec and then it adds the following correction to that already made:

$$\Delta B = -Q4w - Q6P$$

Experimentation with sensitivity factors led to the following values:

$$Q2 = 1.8, \quad Q4 = 2.0, \quad Q6 = .002$$

to give flying characteristics like those of the historical record, when flown with a reaction-time delay of .06 seconds. The reaction time proved to be easy to select. In fact, .04 seconds provided flight control that was clearly more powerful than that of the human pilot, while .08 seconds gave a pilot that had no trouble with the 1905–1907 Flyers, but could not control the 1903–1904 Flyers adequately.

Orville Wright related an occasion, early in his flying career, in which he became so engrossed in lateral control problems that he forgot altogether about his longitudinal control and got into an extreme stall position (Reference 46). It is easy to see, however, how even an experienced pilot, with a machine whose longitudinal control requires the constant reflexes as sharp as those of a baseball hitter, can forget himself long enough to lose control of a machine whose lateral or directional control might be demanding attention, as so often happened in the days of the 1903–1904 Flyers.

54   *Frederick J. Hooven*

The control algorithm resolves into the following, neglecting the offsets of W and Aa:

$$\Delta B = Q2(Q1 - Ap) - Q4 \frac{dAp}{dt} - .Q6\,Im \frac{d^2Ap}{dt^2}$$

$$\Delta B = 1.8(Q1 - Ap) - 2.0 \frac{dAp}{dt} - .56 \frac{d^2Ap}{dt^2}$$

Flyer	Im	Q1*57.3	Q6 × Im
1903	280	4.12	.56
1904 ph 2	295	3.3	.59
1904 ph 3	445	3.3	.89
1905	605	3	1.21

Concluding Remarks; The Simulated Flights

In the following, Figures 16–21 represent the flight of the 1903 Flyer under conditions typical of Kitty Hawk on December 17, 1903. Figures 22–27 represent the flight of the 1903, the 1904 phase 2 and the 1904 phase 3 Flyers, and the 1905 Flyer following perturbation by a one-second elevator pulse followed by normal piloted control as described. Figure 28 shows the flight of the 1905 Flyer in a stalled descent, and Figure 29 shows the 1905 Flyer in its stable regime after certain modifications.

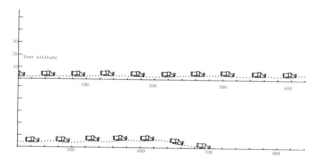

16. Simulated flight under typical Kitty Hawk conditions. Rough landing after 15 seconds, 1903 Flyer.

The Kitty Hawk Flights (Figures 16–21)

On December 17, 1903, the Wrights made four flights. The first three averaged 10 ft/sec over the ground, and lasted approximately 12 seconds, while the last averaged 14.5 ft/sec over the ground, lasting for 59 seconds. All were made against winds that averaged about 34 ft/sec and which were gusting. "Undulation" was a problem, accentuated by the fact that the Flyer's elevator was overbalanced and tended to go to extremes of travel.

The simulated flights were all made at an airspeed of 44 ft/sec against winds that gusted up to 8 ft/sec for a duration of up to 3 seconds, both figures being random numbers. Assumed engine power was initially

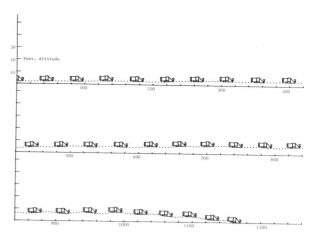

17. Simulated flight under typical Kitty Hawk conditions. Rough landing after 28 seconds, 1903 Flyer.

15, dropping off during the first 10 seconds to 13.8, the steady-state power required for level flight at 44 ft/sec. Altitude is plotted against horizontal distance, the distance being air distance except for Figure 21 where it is over-the-ground distance, assuming a mean wind speed of 30 ft/sec. Altitude is plotted at double the scale of horizontal distance. The diagrammatic graphic Flyers are shown once for each second of

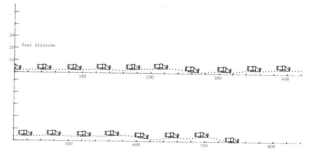

18. Simulated flight under typical Kitty Hawk conditions. Landing after 16 seconds, 1903 Flyer.

flight time, and their pitch angle and angle of their elevator planes are represented as they actually were. The dots indicate the position of the Flyer at the .1 second points.

All flights were made under identical conditions except for the random gusts. It will be noted that of

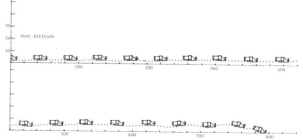

19. Simulated flight under typical Kitty Hawk conditions. Crashing after 17 seconds, 1903 Flyer.

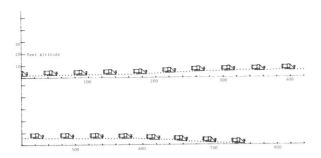

20. Simulated flight under typical Kitty Hawk conditions. Landing after 16 seconds, 1903 Flyer.

the first five flights, four encountered "undulation" before they ended. Of this five, two had normal landings, two had rough landings, and one ended in a crash. A crash is a vertical velocity exceeding 12 ft/sec, a rough landing exceeds 8 ft/sec. Figure 21 shows eight flights, of which four were normal landings, two were rough landings, and two were crashes.

Wind gusts were simulated by arbitrary variations in airspeed, and each gust was followed by one of opposite sign and similar duration so that mean gusting was zero. Gusts strike wings and elevators in the proper sequence, causing the pitch angle to be perturbed, and initiating undulation.

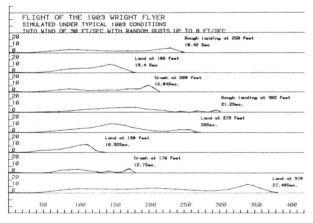

21. "Kitty Hawk" flights, 1903 Flyer.

The Stability Flights (Figures 22–28)

Each flight begins with a fixed elevator position for its first second. The elevator position was proportioned such that a 10°/sec pitching rate was established, following which the normal pilot took over control. In the instance of the 1904 phase 3 Flyer, with its 70 pound ballast weight on the elevator frame, a 10°/sec pitch rate caused amplitudes of such magnitude in pitch that the linear range of elevator lift was exceeded, so a second test was conducted in which the elevator pulse rather than the pulse rate was equated with the tests on the other machines.

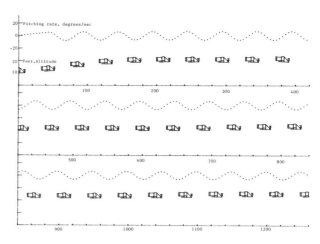

22. Simulated flight of the 1903 Flyer after 10°/sec perturbation. $C_g = 29\%$ chord, 1-second elevator pulse, .76.°

In these tests altitude is plotted against horizontal distance, with altitude being plotted at double the scale of horizontal distance. The dotted line, however, indicates the angular velocity of pitching rather than the machine's altitude. As in the above, the graphic Flyer appears once for each second of flight.

The 1904 phase 1 Flyer behaved so much like the 1903 Flyer that separate tests were not deemed necessary. The phase 2 test shows that by moving

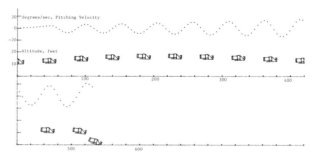

23. Simulated flight of the 1904 Flyer, phase 2 after 10°/sec perturbation. C_g at 32% chord, 1-second elevator pulse = .79.°

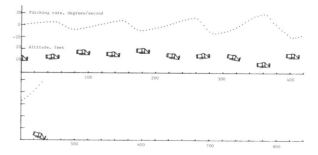

24. Simulated flight of the 1904 Flyer, phase 3 after 10°/sec perturbation. $C_g = 23\%$ chord. (70 lb. ballast on front elevator frame), 1-second elevator pulse = 1.34.°

the center of gravity from 29 percent to 32 percent chord the Wrights put this machine beyond the limits of controllability.

The 1904 phase 3 test shows the effect of the great increase in moment of inertia brought about by the addition of the 70 pound ballast weight on the elevator frame, an increase from 295 sl ft² to 445 sl ft². The 10°/sec pitching rate puts the elevator beyond its range of linear lift, and the unsymmetrical pitching-rate curve shows that the elevator is approaching the stall point during the oscillation. The result of this is a radical reduction in damping with a catastrophic increase in amplitude of pitch.

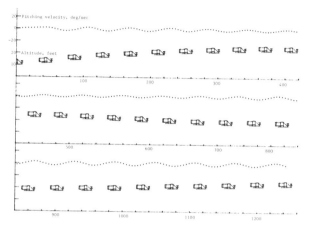

25. Simulated flight of the 1904 Flyer after perturbation by elevator pulse of .78° for one second. C_g = 23% chord, phase 3 with 70 lb ballast weight.

Testing the phase 3 Flyer, with an elevator pulse equal to that impressed on the 1903 and 1904 phase 2 Flyers, shows an oscillation within the limits of linear lift for the elevator. This is the state in which the 1904 Flyer spent most of its flying life.

Tests of the 1905 Flyer with a 10°/sec initial perturbation show quick damping and a rapid reduc-

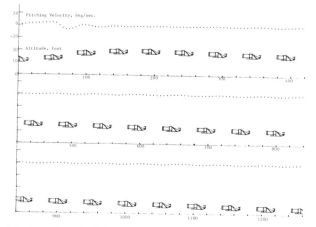

26. Simulated flight of the 1905 Flyer after 10°/sec perturbation. C_g = 18% chord.

tion in amplitude of pitch, with a small residual pitching rate that was characteristic of the 1905 and 1907 machines (Reference 45).

Figures 27 and 28 show the effect of an increase of .02 second in the pilot's reaction time delay with the 1903 and 1905 Flyers. A .06 second time delay is in the same range as those required of a baseball hitter, and an increase in that time from .06 to .08 seconds results in a loss of control of the 1903 Flyer, as shown by Figure 27. A similar increase has almost no detectable effect on the 1905 machine.

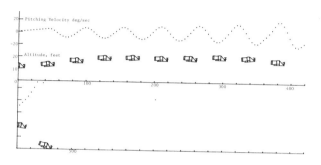

27. Simulated flight of the 1903 Flyer after 10°/sec perturbation, with pilot reaction-time delay of .08 seconds. C_g = 29% chord.

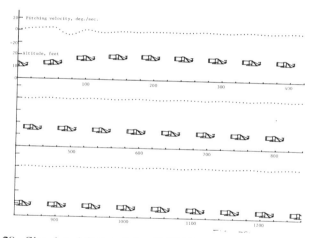

28. Simulated flight of the 1905 Flyer after 10°/sec perturbation, with pilot reaction-time delay of .08 seconds.

The Stalled Descent of the 1905 Flyer (Figure 29)

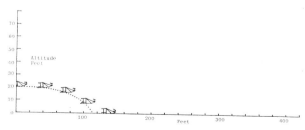

29. Simulated flight of the 1905 Flyer illustrating stall behavior.

The entire rationale of the Wrights' use of the forward elevator is shown by this flight, which required that the pilot be directed to watch pitch angle only. The machine does descend without diving, its angle of attack at landing being 48°. Even so, from 20 feet altitude, it strikes the ground at a vertical velocity of 13 ft/sec, which constitutes a crash.

The Flight of the Modified Flyer 1905 (Figure 30)

For the 1905 Flyer, being my sentimental favorite of all airplanes, I illustrate the effects of a modification similar to those being brought about in certain so-called replicas of Wright Flyers that have taken the air of late, that of a great increase in power over the prototype. The 1905 Flyer is not blessed with low drag; its drag is the equivalent of a barn door size 5 × 9 feet, and, while its historic 20 horsepower would propel it at 34 miles per hour, no less than 250 horsepower would be required to propel it as fast as 80 miles per hour, at which speed its drag is almost equal to its weight. Endowed with thrust of this magnitude many things are possible, one of which is shown in Figure 30.

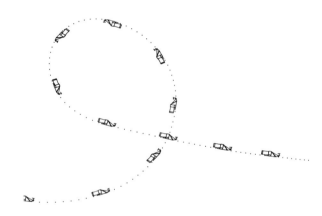

30. Simulated flight of "modified" 1905 Flyer.

Frederick J. Hooven was Professor of Engineering at the Thayer School of Engineering of Dartmouth College. He studied Aeronautical and Mechanical engineering at MIT, receiving his B.S. in 1927. He then worked for the General Motors Research Laboratory and the Army Air Corps. For much of his career, he worked as an independent consultant and inventor and collaborated in the development of the first successful heart-lung machine. In 1956 he joined the Ford Motor Company as an executive engineer for advanced automotive products.

Professor Hooven was a member of the National Academy of Engineering, American Association for the Advancement of Science, American Institute of Aeronautics and Astronautics, Dartmouth Engineering Society, Dayton Engineers Club, Federation of American Scientists, and Sigma Xi. He held thirty-eight U.S. patents and published numerous technical articles.

Frederick J. Hooven died before this work was published.

Notes

1. The term "elevator" is used interchangeably with "horizontal rudder," "horizontal stabilizer," "stabilizer" and "canard." The latter is incorrectly applied to the elevator, being the term that is applied to the machine whose elevator is in front of the wing.

2. Whenever Huffaker refers to "rudder" he means horizontal rudder, or stabilizer, since the 1901 machine had no vertical rudder.

References

1. Gibbs-Smith, Charles H. *The Invention of the Aeroplane.* New York: Taplinger, 1965.

2. McFarland, Marvin W. *The Papers of Wilbur and Orville Wright.* New York: McGraw-Hill, 1953, p. 547.

3. "Aerodynamic Characteristics of Airfoils," NACA Technical Report No. 93, 1919, p. 318.

4. Hooven, Frederick J. "The Wright Brothers Flight-Control System," *Scientific American* 239:5, November 1978, p. 167.

5. Chanute-Huffaker Diary, July–August 1901, pp. 154, 161, 167. Papers of Wilbur and Orville Wright. Library of Congress.

6. Wright, Wilbur, "Some Aeronautical Experiments." *Journal, Western Society of Engineers,* December 1901. In this paper Wilbur describes experiments conducted with the upper wing of the 1901 glider in the wind at Kitty Hawk, in which it was proved that the center of pressure of the wing moves forward as the angle of attack increases, in contradiction to Lilienthal's data.

7. See McFarland, p. 253, letter from Wilbur to George A. Spratt, September 18, 1902.

8. The rearward movement of the center of gravity of the 1904 Flyer in the expectation of improving the pitching tendency has been called a blunder by some, including myself, but I have changed my opinion. The Wrights were not expecting to improve the static stability of the machine, and there is no doubt they were entirely familiar with static stability inasmuch as they were acquainted with the work of Pénaud and they had made and flown many models. They knew that moving the center of gravity to the rear would increase the machine's response to stabilizer movement, and it was entirely reasonable to suppose that this move would help the pitching difficulty.

9. Diary F of Wilbur Wright, 1905, pp. 6–7. Papers of Wilbur and Orville Wright. Library of Congress Archives Folder.

10. Notebook H of Wilbur Wright, p. 16. Papers of Wilbur and Orville Wright. Library of Congress Archives Folder.

11. See McFarland, p. 445, letter from Wilbur to Octave Chanute, July 17, 1904.

12. The drawing, Figure 11, is not authenticated, but it checks in all known details and dimensions with its subject, and the original drawing must have been made by someone with access to the machine itself.

13. See McFarland, p. 938, in a letter from Orville to Wilbur, November 14, 1908.

14. Personal communication from Orville Wright (see p. 3). This is the only personal communication from Mr. Wright I can cite in relevance to the current subject of longitudinal dynamics.

Frederick J. Hooven

15. It is a fact that any machine, whether a canard or not, will descend more or less flat in a stall if its center of gravity is far enough back, but the forward placement of the stabilizer makes this fact intuitively more apparent.

16. See Wright, Wilbur, "Some Aeronautical Experiments." This paper was widely published in Europe and is credited with reviving interest in flying, especially in France, where the first gliders and powered machines clearly derived from the Wrights.

17. Renstrom, Arthur G. "Wilbur and Orville Wright, a Chronology." Washington, D.C.: Library of Congress, 1975.

18. See McFarland, p. 912, letter from Wilbur to Orville, August 15, 1908.

19. Larrabee, E. Eugene, private communication with the author.

20. Munk, Max M. "General Biplane Theory." NACA Technical Report No. 151, 1922.

21. Glauert, H. *Elements of Airfoil and Airscrew Theory*, MacMillen 1943, p. 125.

22. See Glauert, p. 87.

23. Drawings of 1903 Wright brothers Flyer. National Air and Space Museum, Smithsonian Institution, Washington, D.C.

24. Drawings of restored 1905 Wright brothers Flyer, U.S. Air Force, Wright-Patterson Air Force Base, Dayton, Ohio.

25. Abbott, Ira H., and von Doenhoff, Albert E. *Theory of Wing Sections*. New York: Dover Publications, 1959, pp. 66–73.

26. Theodorsen, Theodore. "On the Theory of Wing Sections, with Particular Reference to Lift Distribution." NACA Technical Report No. 383, 1931.

27. Knight, M., and Wentzinger, C.J. "Wind Tunnel Tests on a Series of Wing Models through a Large Angle of Attack Range." NACA Technical Report No. 317, 1929.

28. Bettis, W.H., and Culick, F.E.C. "Wind Tunnel Tests on a ⅙ Scale Model of the Wright Brothers 1903 Flyer Airplane." Guggenheim Aeronautical Laboratory, California Institute of Technology Report No. 1034, Pasadena, Calif., 1982, p. 20.

29. McPhail, C.D. "Textbook Analysis of the Longitudinal Characteristics of the 1903 Wright Flyer." Private communication, 1981, p. V–1.

30. Wood, K.D. *Technical Aerodynamics*, New York: McGraw-Hill, 1935.

31. "Aerodynamic Characteristics of Airfoils, V." NACA Technical Report No. 286, 1928, REF 649.

32. See Abbott, et al., p. 111.

33. Millikan, Clark B. *Aerodynamics of the Airplane*. London: Wiley, 1941, p. 47.

34. Silverstein, A., Katzoff S., and Bullivant Kenneth W. "Downwash and Wake Behind Plain and Flapped Airfoils." NACA Technical Report No. 651, 1938, Figure 18.

35. Notebook K of Wilbur and Orville Wright, 1903.

Papers of Wilbur and Orville Wright. Library of Congress Archives Folder.

36. Orville Wright to Charles Taylor, November 23, 1903. The Papers of Wilbur and Orville Wright. Library of Congress Archives Folder.

37. See McFarland, Appendix pp. 1212, 1213.

38. Chenowith, Opie. "Power Plants built by the Wright Brothers." *SAE Quarterly Transactions* 5, January 1951, pp. 14–17.

39. Noyes, Richard W. "Pressure Distribution Tests on a Series of Clark Y Biplane Cellules with Special Reference to Stability." NACA Technical Report No. 417, 1932.

40. Munk, Max M. "Air Forces on a Systematic Series of Biplane and Triplane Cellule Models. NACA Technical Report No. 256, 1926.

41. Crowley, J.W., Jr. "Pressure Distribution over a Wing and Tail Rib of a VE-7 and of a TS Airplane in Flight." NACA Technical Report No. 257, 1927.

42. The first of the 1907 Flyers was built along with the 1904 and 1905 machines in the spring of 1904 (see McFarland, p. 442, note 1), which makes it unlikely that it had a unique wing section. The drawing in Figure 11 is of unknown origin and unauthenticated, but it checks what is known of that machine, and it shows a rounded leading edge similar to those on other Wright machines. It has therefore been concluded that, at least in this respect, the Eiffel 10 is not a representative Wright wing section.

43. The Bettis and Culick report shows that the combination of wing and stabilizer has zero lift at $-3.4°$ angle of attack with the stabilizer incidence being 0. It has been assumed that both sections exhibit under-wing burbles, and that their true angles of zero lift will bear the same proportion as their computed values of a_o and a_{oh}, which are -4.84 and -2.8 respectively. Since the sum of both lifts is 0 at $-3.4°$ it can be said that

$$Cl = -Kh \text{ and } \frac{.062}{R}(3.4 - a_{oh}') = .063(3.4 - a_o')$$

$$3.4\, a_{oh}' = 9.83\, a_o' - 33.422$$

We assume that

$$\frac{a_{t_h} - a_{oh}'}{a_t - a_o'} = \frac{a_{t_h} - a_{oh}}{a_t - a_o} = \frac{.3 + 2.8}{1.0828 + 4.84} = .5234$$

$$a_{oh}' = .2667 + .5234\, a_o' = 36.822 - 9.83 a_o'$$

then $a_o = -3.58$ and $a_{oh} = -2.14$

44. Wilbur to Orville, August 9, 1908. Papers of Orville and Wilbur Wright. Library of Congress, Archives Folder.

45. This effect is seen in the first moving picture ever taken from a moving airplane, a Bioscope cinema of which a copy resides in the National Air and Space Museum, Washington, D.C.

46. Diary B of Orville Wright, September 20, 1902, in which he describes forgetting to operate the elevator in his concentration on a problem with the lateral control. The Papers of Wilbur and Orville Wright. Library of Congress, Archives Folder.

Table 1
Dimensions of 1903 and 1904 Flyers

Wing Span	40.33 ft
Wing Chord	6.5 ft
Wing Gap	6.0 ft
Wing Area	510 sq ft
Wing Aspect Ratio ($2b^2/S$)	6.47
Elevator Span	12.0 ft
Elevator Chord	2.54 ft
Elevator Gap	2.17 ft
Elevator Area	52.75 sq ft
Elevator Aspect Ratio	5.46
Elevator Moment Arm from Leading Edge	7.32 ft
Rudder Height	7.0 ft
Rudder Length (chord)	1.5 ft
Rudder Area	10.26 sq ft
Rudder Moment Arm from Leading Edge	11.5 ft
Cg Position from Leading Edge	
1903, 1904 ph.1	1.89 ft, 29%
1904 ph.2	2.21 ft, 34%
1904 ph.3	1.42 ft, 21.8%
Flying Weight	
1903	750 lb
1904, ph.1,2	784 lb
1904, ph.3 with 70 lb wt	854 lb
Weight per Unit Wing Area	
1903	1.47 lb/sq ft
1904, ph. 1,2	1.54 lb/sq ft
1904, ph.3	1.67 lb/sq
Propeller Diameter	8.5 ft

Table 2
Dimensions of 1905 and 1907 Flyers

Wing Span	40.33 ft
Wing Chord	6.5 ft
Wing Gap	6.0 ft
Wing Area	510 sq ft
Wing Aspect Ratio ($2b^2/S$)	6.47
Eleavator Span	15.63 ft
Elevator Chord	3.0 ft
Elevator Gap	3.0 ft
Elevator Area	83 sq ft
Elevator Aspect Ratio	5.89
Elevator Moment Arm from Leading Edge	11.7 ft
Rudder Height	7.0 ft
Rudder Length (chord)	2.25 ft
Rudder Area	15.5 sq ft
Rudder Moment Arm from Leading Edge	11.18 ft
Cg Position from Leading	
Edge 1905	1.22 ft, 18.8%
1907 1 man (1)	1.0 ft, 15.32%
1970 1 man (2)	1.1 ft, 17%
1907 2 men (1)	.87 ft, 13.34%
1907 2 men (2)	1.07 ft, 16.39%
Flying Weight 1905	914 lb
1907 1 man	1041 lb
1907 2 men	1186 lb
Weight per Unit Wing Area,	
1905	1.79 lb
1907 1 man	2.04 lb
1907 2 men	2.32 lb
Propeller Diameter	8.5 ft

Table 3
Thin-Wing Functions

X	1E5*Y	F1(X)	F2(X)	F3(X)
0.0125	358	2.9012	8.7756	113.15
0.025	712	2.091	6.0848	39.7306
0.0375	1065	1.7407	4.8688	21.469
0.05	1410	1.5373	4.1294	13.8363
0.0625	1744	1.4026	3.6147	9.8186
0.075	2063	1.3064	3.2271	7.4034
0.0875	2363	1.2345	2.9196	5.8198
0.1	2643	1.1789	2.6666	4.7156
0.1125	2908	1.135	2.4526	3.9096
0.125	3158	1.0999	2.2677	3.2999
0.1375	3393	1.0716	2.1052	2.8252
0.15	3613	1.0487	1.9603	2.4471
0.1625	3818	1.0302	1.8297	2.1397
0.175	4008	1.0154	1.7106	1.8857
0.1875	4188	1.0037	1.6012	1.6728
0.2	4360	0.9947	1.5	1.492
0.2125	4518	0.988	1.4056	1.3368
0.225	4664	0.9835	1.3171	1.2021
0.2375	4798	0.9809	1.2336	1.0842
0.25	4920	0.9801	1.1547	0.9801
0.2625	5030	0.9809	1.0795	0.8875
0.275	5128	0.9832	1.0078	0.8044
0.2875	5214	0.987	0.939	0.7295
0.3	5290	0.9922	0.8728	0.6615
0.3125	5350	0.9988	0.809	0.5993
0.325	5398	1.0068	0.7472	0.5421
0.3375	5430	1.016	0.6873	0.4892
0.35	5448	1.0267	0.6289	0.44
0.3625	5456	1.0386	0.572	0.3939
0.375	5461	1.0519	0.5163	0.3506
0.3875	5464	1.0667	0.4618	0.3096
0.4	5464	1.0829	0.4082	0.2707
0.4125	5461	1.1005	0.3554	0.2334
0.425	5456	1.1198	0.3034	0.1976
0.4375	5446	1.1407	0.2519	0.1629
0.45	5431	1.1633	0.201	0.1292
0.4625	5411	1.1877	0.1504	0.0963
0.475	5386	1.2141	0.1001	0.0639
0.4875	5351	1.2425	0.05	0.0318
0.5	5306	1.2732	0	0
0.5125	5256	1.3062	−0.0501	−0.0319
0.525	5201	1.3419	−0.1002	−0.064
0.5375	5141	1.3803	−0.1505	−0.0964
0.55	5071	1.4218	−0.2011	−0.1293
0.5625	4991	1.4666	−0.252	−0.163
0.575	4901	1.515	−0.3035	−0.1977
0.5875	4806	1.5675	−0.3555	−0.2335
0.6	4706	1.6243	−0.4083	−0.2708
0.6125	4606	1.6861	−0.4619	−0.3097
0.625	4501	1.7533	−0.5164	−0.3507
0.6375	4391	1.8266	−0.5721	−0.394
0.65	4271	1.9067	−0.629	−0.4401
0.6625	4138	1.9945	−0.6874	−0.4893
0.675	3997	2.091	−0.7473	−0.5422
0.6875	3854	2.1975	−0.8091	−0.5994
0.7	3709	2.3153	−0.8729	−0.6616

Frederick J. Hooven

0.7125	3563	2.4462	−0.9391	−0.7296
0.725	3416	2.5922	−1.0079	−0.8045
0.7375	3268	2.7559	−1.0796	−0.8876
0.75	3120	2.9404	−1.1548	−0.9802
0.7625	2972	3.1494	−1.2337	−1.0843
0.775	2824	3.3878	−1.3172	−1.2022
0.7875	2674	3.6617	−1.4057	−1.3369
0.8	2520	3.9788	−1.5	−1.4921
0.8125	2370	4.3494	−1.6013	−1.6729
0.825	2216	4.787	−1.7107	−1.8858
0.8375	2058	5.3097	−1.8298	−2.1398
0.85	1894	5.9429	−1.9604	−2.4472
0.8625	1724	6.7222	−2.1053	−2.8253
0.875	1546	7.6998	−2.2678	−3.3
0.8875	1358	8.9543	−2.4527	−3.9097
0.9	1160	10.6103	−2.6667	−4.7157
0.9125	952	12.8742	−2.9197	−5.8199
0.925	734	16.1133	−3.2272	−7.4035
0.9375	526	21.0398	−3.6148	−9.8187
0.95	396	29.21	−4.1295	−13.8364
0.9625	297	44.6788	−4.8689	−21.4691
0.975	198	81.5523	−6.0849	−39.7307
0.9875	99	229.2	−8.7757	−113.15

Table 4

Pankhurst's constants and upper and lower ordinates of the 1903 wing listed against chordal station.

X	A	B	L	U
0	0	0	.875	.875
0.025	2.11	−0.156	.25	2.0
0.05	1.56	−0.104	.9	2.63
0.1	2.41	−0.124	1.8	3.50
0.2	2.94	−0.074	3.13	4.87
0.3	2.88	−0.009	3.83	5.34
0.4	3.13	0.045	3.94	5.35
0.5	3.67	0.101	3.75	5.07
0.6	4.69	0.17	3.13	4.51
0.7	6.72	0.273	2.50	3.65
0.8	11.75	0.477	1.59	2.62
0.9	21.72	0.786	.59	1.32
0.95	99.85	3.026	−.02	.605
1.00	0	0	−.625	0

Table 5

Coefficients of lift, drag, pitching moment for the wing and lift for the uncambered stabilizer section, listed for angles of attack from −4 to +30.

a	Cl	Cd	Cm	K1*
−4	−0.088	0.091	−0.054	−0.0253
−3	0.052	0.084	−0.072	−0.019
−2	0.142	0.077	−0.101	−0.0127
−1	0.225	0.075	−0.127	−0.0064
0	0.3	0.073	−0.148	0
1	0.367	0.075	−0.165	0.0063
2	0.43	0.08	−0.18	0.0126
3	0.493	0.084	−0.195	0.0189
4	0.556	0.091	−0.21	0.0252
5	0.618	0.1	−0.224	0.0314
6	0.68	0.109	−0.239	0.0375
7	0.74	0.122	−0.254	0.0433
8	0.8	0.136	−0.269	0.049
9	0.857	0.152	−0.284	0.054
10	0.912	0.168	−0.299	0.0586
11	0.963	0.19	−0.313	0.0622
12	1.01	0.217	−0.328	0.0646
13	1.05	0.245	−0.337	0.0655
14	1.082	0.272	−0.344	0.0645
15	1.103	0.301	−0.35	0.061
16	1.11	0.331	−0.353	0.0546
17	1.101	0.353	−0.35	0.0527
18	1.072	0.376	−0.345	0.0517
19	1.017	0.387	−0.338	0.0517
20	0.932	0.399	−0.334	0.0517
21	0.81	0.415	−0.319	0.0506
22	0.76	0.43	−0.308	0.0496
23	0.73	0.443	−0.297	0.0486
24	0.7	0.457	−0.286	0.0475
25	0.7	0.468	−0.286	0.0465
26	0.7	0.48	−0.286	0.0455
27	0.7	0.493	−0.286	0.0444
28	0.7	0.507	−0.286	0.0434
29	0.705	0.518	−0.286	0.0423
30	0.71	0.53	−0.286	0.0413

* Stabilizer lift coefficient is referred to the wing area for the 1903 Flyer.

Table 6

Mean line, trailing section of 1903 rib, deflection with maximum of 1% at trailing edge. The chord line is drawn for the deflected rib, so the undeflected coordinates are shown below the chord line.

X	Undeflected Ordinates	Deflected Ordinates	Deflection ($y \times 10^5$)
0.625	3798	3798	0
0.6375	3680	3725	44
0.65	3552	3642	89
0.6625	3411	3545	134
0.675	3262	3441	178
0.6875	3111	3334	223
0.7	2958	3226	268
0.7125	2803	3116	312
0.725	2648	3005	357
0.7375	2491	2893	402
0.75	2334	2781	446
0.7625	2177	2668	491
0.775	2019	2556	536
0.7875	1860	2441	581
0.8	1696	2322	625
0.8125	1537	2207	670
0.825	1373	2065	692
0.8375	1205	1919	714
0.85	1031	1767	736
0.8625	850	1608	758
0.875	662	1442	780
0.8875	463	1265	802
0.9	254	1078	824
0.9125	35	881	846
0.925	−194	674	868
0.9375	−414	477	890
0.95	−555	357	912
0.9625	−667	268	934
0.975	−778	178	956
0.9875	−889	89	978

Nomenclature

A = Effective monoplane aspect ratio

A = Pankhurst's integration constant for Ao

Aa,aa = Angle of attack, radians and degrees

Ab,ab = Absolute angle of attack (Aa − Az) radians and degrees

Af,af = Flight path slope angle, radians and degrees

Ah,ah = Incidence angle of stabilizer

Ai,ai = Incidence angle of wing

Ao,ao = Angle of zero lift

Ao',ao' = Effective value of ao with under-wing burbles

Ap,ap = Airplane pitch angle

At,at = Theodorsen's "ideal" angle of attack

B = Pankhurst's integration constant for Cq

B = Stabilizer-to-wing angle, degrees +10 = Ah − Aa + 10

B = Munk's ratio of 2-D to 3-D biplane lift

Be = Effective stabilizer angle corrected for pitching rate

B3 = Automatic-pilot reaction-time delay factor

B7 = Automatic pilot offset for pitching rate correction radians/sec

Cd = Drag coefficient for entire airplane except stabilizer

Cg = Center of gravity longitudinal coordinate, percent chord

Cl,L(I) = Lift coefficient for wing

Cm = Pitching-moment coefficient

Cmac = Pitching-moment coefficient about aerodynamic center

C = Pitching-moment coefficient about Cg

Cq = Pitching-moment coefficient about quarter-chord point

Dg = Drag, pounds for complete airplane except stabilizer

DL = Distance from leading edge to stabilizer $\frac{1}{3}$ chord, percent chord

Fd = $\frac{1}{2}$da*S, aerodynamic factor

F(I) = Automatic-pilot time-delay count

Gv = Random-wind maximum velocity for gusts ft/sec

H = Engine-shaft horsepower, assuming propulsion efficiency of 72.7%

Im = Airplane longitudinal moment of inertia, slugs feet^2

I,l2 = Angle of attack +10 and fractional degrees for data matrix

J,J2 = Stabilizer angle +10 and fractional degrees for data matrix

Kl,K(I) = Stabilizer lift coefficient for uncambered section

Kh = Stabilizer lift coefficient corrected for camber

Lz = Total airplane lift for stabilizer and wing, pounds

L = Lower-surface ordinate for airfoil section, chord/100

N = Effective camber reduction factor for under-wing burbles

N = Elapsed time count of iteration period in computer program

P = Pitching moment, pounds feet

Pd = Dynamic pressure, $SV^2da/2$

Q = Input variable for program control codes

Q1 = Target value of angle (ai + ap + af)/2 for automatic pilot, degrees

Q2 = Sensitivity index for pilot for angles of pitch and attack

Q4 = Sensitivity index for pilot for pitching motion

R = Ratio of wing area to stabilizer area

R = Theodorsen's value of $(x(1 − x))^{1/2}$

S = Wing surface area, square feet

T = Elapsed time of flight, seconds

Th = Thrust pounds

U,Ul = Stabilizer angle of attack, degrees +10 and fractional degrees

U = Upper-surface ordinate for airfoil section percent chord

V,Vh = Airspeed, feet per second, at wing and at stabilizer

Vv = Vertical component of velocity of airplane

Wt = Weight of airplane, pounds

W,w = Angular velocity of pitching motion, degrees and radians/sec

Y = Thin-wing airfoil maximum ordinate, percent chord

Yh = Stabilizer section maximum ordinate, percent chord

Z = Altitude of flight, feet

b = Wing span, feet

ch = Wing chord, feet

cp = Center of pressure, percent chord

dV = Airspeed increment, ft/sec/sec

da = Air density, slugs/cu ft

e,u = Variables used in computation of differential lift coefficient

g = Wing gap, feet

p = Power of sl in lift-coefficient equation

p = Differential coefficient of profile lift

q = Differential coefficient of induced lift

r = Radius of airfoil section leading edge, percent chord

SO,so = Lift-curve slope, of 2–D biplane per radian and per degree

Sl,sl = Lift-curve slope, of 3–D biplane per radian and per degree

t = Iteration time for computer program, seconds

x = Distance along chord line, percent chord

xp = Value of x as transformed for profile lift

xq = Value of x as transformed for induced lift

xe = Value of x associated with given value of e

y = Ordinate of mean-line thin-wing airfoil section, percent chord

yh = Ordinate for stabilizer section, percent chord

ye = Effective value of y as reduced by under-wing turbulence

z1 = Vertical coordinate of cener of lift, percent chord

z2 = Vertical coordinate of center of thrust, percent chord

z3 = Vertical coordinate of center of drag, percent chord

as subscript p applies to profile lift

as subscript i applies to induced lift

as subscript h applies to stabilizer.

APPENDIX 1

The Wright Wing Section

The five Wright canards all had wing sections of the same general shape, thin, highly cambered, tapering from front to rear, yet all differing in small ways. The 1904 Flyer, destroyed without drawings ever having been made, was reported by the Wrights to have a camber of $1/25$ instead of the approximately $1/20$ of the other machines. Replica ribs of the 1903 and 1905 machines were built in the course of this investigation, as shown in Figure 31. The 1905 rib is also probably typical of the 1904 and 1907 models since all three were begun at the same time in the spring of 1904. These two airfoils are aerodynamically alike.

The Eiffel 10 section is labeled "Wright," and it resembles the 1903 and 1905 sections, except for its leading edge which is a vertical line with sharp corners at the intersections of the upper and lower surfaces, in contrast to the semicircular leading edge of the 1903 section and the rounded one of the 1905. This deviation from the Wrights' other practice does not seem to be characteristic of the 1907 machine from which the section was presumably taken (Reference 42). As I will show in later discussions, this feature makes it inadvisable to draw conclusions about the 1903 and 1905 wings from the Eiffel data on the #10 section.

The 1903 and 1905 sections have front spars 1.75″ deep, rear spars 1.25″ deep. The 1903 section tapers more or less uniformly from just behind the front spar to the trailing edge, being just 1.25″ deep at the rear spar location. As a result the rib is built in two pieces, which are connected across the spar by thin metal strips (Figure 31d). The 1905 rib is heavier, with $1/4″ \times 1/2″$ cap strips instead of the $1/4″ \times 3/8″$ of the 1903, and its thickness remains at 1.75″ until a point aft of the rear spar, so that the rib is built in one piece and its cap strips span the rear spar. The rib is attached to the front spar by metal strips in both instances.

The two ribs differ in trailing-edge configuration also. They accurately outline the airfoil section except at the trailing edge, where the ribs have substantial thickness, whereas the actual trailing edges are wires attached to the ribs. In the case of the 1903 rib, it is attached to the upper surface at the trailing edge, which gives the mean line a slight upturn over its last 5%, while the 1905 trailing edge wire is attached to the mid-point of the rib trailing edge. The 1903 rib has, as a result of this slope reduction, lower values of a_o and c_m.

Existing drawings do not exactly represent the Wright contours. Neither rib has in its list of ordinates those of the .025, .05, and .95 stations, which must be learned from a detailed scale drawing of the rib, or from a replica rib. The rib strips are of ash, which

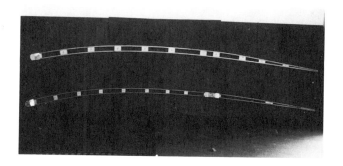

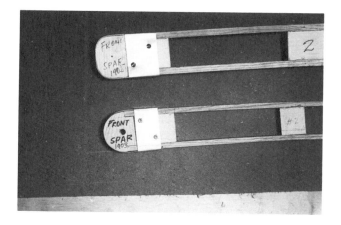

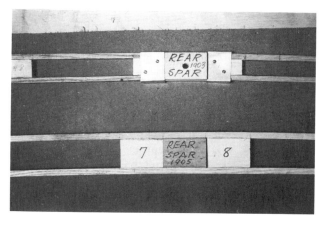

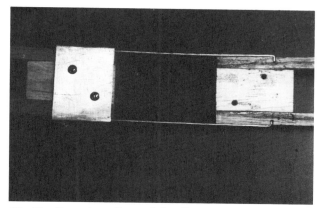

31. Replica wing ribs and details.

does not take placidly to being wrestled around arbitrary corners, so that it was necessary to make some very slight adjustments in the given dimensions in certain spots, although these are entirely negligible in aerodynamic effects. The 1903 drawings (Reference 23) give upper and lower ordinates for the 10% stations, while the 1905 drawings (Reference 25) give lower ordinates only for each 6″ station, leaving the upper ordinates to be established by the detailed dimensions of the rib.

A lack of sufficient spacing blocks aft of the rear spar gives the 1903 rib a considerable degree of compliance, 2.3 lb/in as measured directly at the trailing edge. It was at first feared this would have an appreciable effect on the aerodynamics of the section. However, it proved that the amount of the deflection was less than had been originally estimated because the lift pressures were less at the section trailing edge, and the deflections had less than the estimated effect because of the peculiar "parallel link" nature of the deflection, with less than expected angular deflection of the trailing edge (see Figure 37 and Table 6).

For purposes of integration the ordinates of the 1903 mean line were interpolated to 80 segments. Finite-difference methods were used to minimize sudden changes in curvature. These ordinates are given in Table 3, and the section, as well as its mean line, are shown in Figure 32. The mean-line was derived from the section ordinates as follows:

$$y = \frac{L + U}{2} - \frac{L_0 + U_0}{2}(1 - x)$$

where $y_1 = U_1 = 0$

The chord line of this section passes through the upper surface instead of the lower surface at the trailing edge. The equivalent angle of attack for the mean line is a $+ .47°$ for equivalent aerodynamics, and that amount has been added to bring the section to the more conventional configuration.

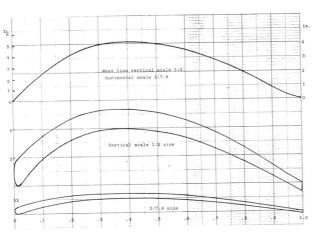

32. 1903 Flyer wing section.

APPENDIX 2

Aerodynamics

A. Lift

Munk's "General Biplane Theory" (Reference 20) tabulates the factors that apply to the lift of 2-dimensional biplanes as functions of those of 2-dimensional monoplanes. These are functions of g/c, and for the Wright g/c of .93 he gives B = .84. Taking the monoplane lift as $Cl = 2\pi Ab_0$ results in a lift-curve slope of $Sl = 1.68$ for the 2-dimensional biplane.

For the 3-dimensional monoplane with elliptical lift distribution Glauert (Reference 21) shows that

$$Ab_0 - Ab_1 = \frac{Cl}{\pi A} \quad \text{where } A = b^2/S$$

where Ab_0 and AB_1 are 2-d

and 3-d values of Ab

Dividing through by Cl gives

$$\frac{1}{So} = \frac{1}{Sl} + \frac{1}{\pi A}$$

Glauert then provides the factor t to account for the rectangular wing for which

$$\frac{1}{So} = \frac{1}{Sl} + \frac{1}{\pi A}(1 + t)$$

and t has a value of .166. However, the rounded wing tips of the 1903 Flyer remove it from the category of rectangular wings and I have arbitrarily reduced that quantity to .12.

Munk tabulates Equivalent Monoplane Span factors for biplanes in terms of g/b, and for the 1903 Flyer's g/b of .148 he gives K = 1.3 so that the Equivalent Monoplane Aspect Ratio becomes

$$A = \frac{(1.13 \times 40.33)^2}{510} = 4.072$$

and $\quad \dfrac{1}{SI} = \dfrac{1}{1.68\pi} + \dfrac{1}{4.072\pi} \times 1.12 = .277$

$$Sl = 3.61 \text{ and } sl = .063$$

The 1903 wing ordinates were interpolated to provide 80 chordal segments for integration by the method of Glauert (Reference 22) to provide angle of zero lift (Az = −4.815) and coefficient of pitching moment (Cq = −.0997). For comparison purposes and for analysis of sections with fewer available ordinate values, the method of Pankhurst, as cited by Abbott (Reference 25), was also used. Pankhurst lists a series of integration constants, for the 10% chordal stations plus the .025, .05, and .95 stations, such that

$$ao = \sum_{x=0}^{1} A(U + L) = 2 \sum_{x=0}^{1} Ay$$

where $y = \dfrac{U + L}{2} - \dfrac{Uo + Lo}{2}(1 - x)$

$$- \dfrac{Ul + Ll}{2} x \quad y1 = 0 = y0$$

$$Cq = \sum_{x=0}^{1} B(U + L) = 2 \sum_{x=0}^{1} By$$

By this measure $ao = -4.79$ and $Cq = -.0997$

Glauert's integrations were performed by computer summation of the 80 chordal segments. He showed that

(1)
$$A_o = -\int_0^1 yfl\,(x)\,dx$$

$$Cq = 2u0 - \frac{\pi}{2} Az$$

where $u0 = \int_0^1 yf2(x)dx$

Theodorsen (Reference 26) separates lift into two components, one of which is in proportion to wing curvature only and is invariant with angle of attack, which he calls the "ideal" lift and which I have called the "profile" lift. It operates at a fixed center of pressure whose position determines the pitch coefficient of the wing. The other component, which I call the "induced" lift, is in direct proportion to absolute angle of attack, and it operates at the aerodynamic center. The angle at which the induced lift is zero is called the "ideal" angle of attack, and it is characterized by an absence of flow discontinuities about the leading edge of the thin-wing section. Theodorsen shows that

(2)
$$A_t = \int_0^1 = yf3(x)dx$$

where $f1(x) = \dfrac{1}{R(1-x)}$ and $R = (x(1 - x))^{1/2}$.

$$f2(x) = \frac{1 - 2x}{R}$$

and $f3(x) = \dfrac{1 - 2x}{2R^3}$

The 80 mean-line ordinates along the chord from $x = .0125$ to $x = .9875$ are summed according to the above functions to obtain ao, Cq and differential coefficients for lift distributions. At the same time actual forces are integrated and with them the deflections of the rib trailing edge. From the differential lift coefficients and their chordal positions the pitch-

ing-moment coefficients are summed. Separate sets of figures are kept for profile and induced components of lift.

Theodorsen's procedures are used for the computation of the differential lift coefficients. He shows that for the profile lift

(3)
$$p = 4R \frac{de}{dx} + \frac{2}{R}[e - eo + (eo - 2e + e1)x]$$

where $e(xe) = \dfrac{1}{\Pi} \int_0^1 \dfrac{ydx}{R(xe - x)}$

$$e1 = -Ao$$

and $e0 = 2at - e1$

Pressure coefficients for induced lift are

(4)
$$q = \frac{4R}{x}(a - at)$$

Although f_1, f_2, f_3 all become infinite at $x = 0$ and $x = 1$, for ordinary leading edges the integrand approaches zero faster than x/c in equations (1) and (2) and at the leading edge in equation (2). Since (2) tends to infinity at the trailing edge, it is integrated only from $x = 0$ to $x = .95$, then the function dBo is added to the result, assuming that the trailing edge and leading edge are of the form

$$y = A + Bx + Cx^2$$

Accordingly $dBo = .964y_{.95} - .0964 \dfrac{dy}{dx_c}$

where $\dfrac{dy}{dx_c}$ is the slope of the mean line at $x = 1$

Similarly (3) is integrated from $x = .05$ to $x = .95$ with added

$$dAo = .467(y_{.95} - y_{.05}) - .0472 \left(\frac{dy}{dxc} - \frac{dy}{dxe} \right)$$

where $\dfrac{dy}{dxe}$ is the slope of the mean line at $x = 0$

Equation (4) becomes infinite at $x = 0$ so Theodorsen substitutes

$$po = 4 \frac{(aa - at)}{(2r/c)^{1/2}}$$, r being the leading edge radius

Wing-rib deflections were computed from measured compliance of the replica rib, which was 2.3 lb/in as applied to the trailing edge. Deflections, as shown in Figure 37, with a double exposure showing the deflected rib superimposed on the undeflected, show relatively little angular deflection, which explains why the aerodynamic effects of the deflection were much less than originally estimated. Lift coefficient vs. angle of attack was affected to a small degree as shown by the dotted lines on Figure 33. Since lift and moment were affected almost equally, pitching moment was little affected as it is plotted against lift coefficient. Aerodynamic effects of deflection were computed by changing the ordinates in accordance with measured deflections, which are tabulated in Table 6.

Inter-wing forces, resulting from mutual repulsion forces, having no resultant, were not given further consideration.

Realistic flight simulation demands more than just a lift-curve slope, and theoretical guidance is difficult in the construction of realistic-looking wing lift curves. Knight and Wentzinger (Reference 27) have in a series of tests of biplane configurations using the Clark Y section, recorded their lift and drag forces from $-39°$ to $+90°$ angles of attack. Their lift curve from $-5°$ to $+21°$ is closely approximated by the following

$$Cl = Slab - Kab^p \qquad \text{where } p = 6$$

then $\quad dCl/da = Sl - pKab^{p-1}$

Assuming the maximum lift will be at $a = 16$ ($ab = 20.84$) at which point

$$\frac{dCl}{dAa} = 0,$$

from which it is determined that $k = 4.012 \times 10^{-7}$. The resulting lift-coefficient curve is plotted on Figure 33. Above normal flying angles the wing properties are those of Knight, et al., of interest in simulating the behavior of the canard configuration under stalled conditions, because of the Wrights' interest in the configuration for its resistance to diving after a stall. This subject is discussed at greater length under "Concluding Remarks; The Simulated Flights."

It will be seen that two lines are drawn for the lift curve in Figure 33 for angles less than At, one of which intersects the 0 lift line at -4.84, the theoretical angle of zero lift. The heavy line curves inward from the theoretical straight line to intersect 0 lift at -3.58. This value of a_0 has been derived from the study "Wind-Tunnel Tests of a ⅙ Scale Model of the Wright Brothers 1903 Flyer Airplane" by Bettis and Culick (Reference 28), who reported lift only for the complete machine with stabilizer.

McPhail (Reference 29), in his "Textbook Analysis of the Longitudinal Characteristics of the 1903 Wright Flyer," attributes this to the presence of underwing burbles, citing Wood (Reference 30), who remarked about such burbles and attributed their effect to an effective thickening of the wing section, with reduction in mean camber, because of effective reduction in the camber of the lower surface of the section. There is, however, no way in which this effect can be related to angle of attack for accurate computation.

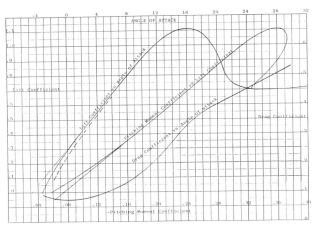

33. Aerodynamics of 1903 Flyer airfoil section.

The same reduction of the numerical value of a^o may be seen on other tests of early wing sections with high camber and small section thickness, such as the Eiffel 10 and the Gottingen 483 (Reference 31), whose lift curves are seen in Figure 34. The latter shows $ao' = -4$ where $a = -5.29$. The effect is more pronounced for the Eiffel 10, owing to its sharp-edged leading edge, where

$$ao' = -2.85 \text{ for } ao = -5.53.$$

Modification of the mean-line ordinates to reproduce the effect of the under-wing burbles was limited to the range of angles between at and ao where Cli is negative since it was assumed that no burbles would exist at the ideal angle of attack. Camber reduction was arranged to take place progressively over the range, and to be at its maximum at the section leading edge, falling off toward the trailing edge.

$$ye = y - n(1 - x)\left(\frac{ap - aa}{ap - ao'}\right)^2$$
$$= y - .833y(y - x)\left(\frac{1.0828 - aa}{4.6228}\right)^2$$

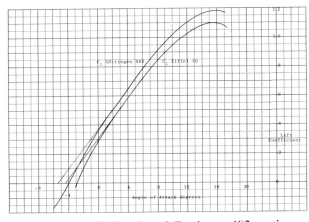

34. Lift curves, Eiffel 10 and Gottingen 483 section.

Frederick J. Hooven

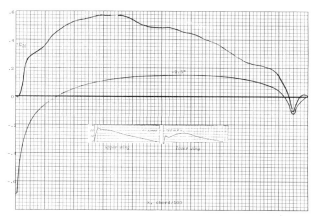

35. Lift pressure distribution, 1903 Flyer airfoil section.

where n has been arbitrarily chosen so that $Cl_i = -Cl_p$ at $a = -3.58$. The multiplying factor was squared to provide a curved line that resembles those of test reports rather than a pair of intersecting straight lines.

The resulting lift and pitching-moment coefficients are plotted in Figure 33 and tabulated in Table 5. Lift-pressure differentials as plotted in Figure 35 clearly show the effects of the trailing edge slope reduction in the negative pressures seen around the 95% chord point.

B. Pitching Moments

Biplane theory does not provide the basis for a consistent theory of biplane pitching moments. While Munk (Reference 20) makes the distinction between Cl_i and Cl_p, he defines their limits differently from Theodorsen (who wrote 10 years later) and in terms that involve a contradiction. Cl_p is the lift that occurs when $cp = .5$ and equals

$$Cl_p = 2 \sin ab B^{1/2} \qquad Cl_i = 2 abB$$

However, at $aa = ao$ it is necessary that the two components of lift be equal and opposite, and the two cannot be equal and be the product of different factors, B and $B^{1/2}$. Munk himself does not pursue the point and in his summary tables he lists the 2-dimensional biplane lift factor as B.

However, Munk and Glauert agree that pitching moments for biplanes are substantially unaltered from their monoplane values in their relation to lift coefficient, although they cannot remain unchanged in their relation to angle of attack, which is of interest in considerations of longitudinal dynamics. For this to be true it follows that the centers of pressure be farther to the rear in the biplane than in the monoplane, since the lift coefficients are smaller. Glauert (Reference 21, p. 180) remarks that the aerodynamic center of the biplane moves forward from $x = .25$ to

$x = .219$. Munk (Reference 20, p. 484) puts this point at $X = .231$ for $g/c = .93$.

With the integration procedures of Glauert and Theodorsen set up, it was easy to integrate for pitching moments. It is useful to integrate section lift differentials separately from those of induced lift, as well as separate lift coefficients.

$$Cm = \int_0^1 p\,dx + \int_0^1 q\,dx$$

Cl_p acts at a fixed center of pressure and is invariable with angle of attack, while Cl_i acts also at a fixed center of pressure but is a function of absolute angle of attack.

Consequently

$$Cm = Cl_p \cdot cp_p + Cl_i \cdot cp_i$$

and

$$Cq = Cl_p (cp_p - cp_i)$$

and the aerodynamic center is cp_i

Moment summations for the monoplane wing show $cp_i = .2614$ and $cp_p = .406$. To provide the changes for the biplane wing xp and xq have been transformed as follows:

$$xp = x(1 - k1) + k1x^{1/2}$$

$xq = x(1 - k2) + k2x^2$ where k1 and k2 are arbitrarily chosen to change cp_p from .406 to .4362 and cp_i from .2614 to .2418.

These figures are less than theory calls for, but more in line with test results such as Knight and Wentzinger (Reference 27), Noyes (Reference 39), and Munk (Reference 40), who tested biplane cellules.

Moments are plotted in Figure 33. In Figure 35 are shown pressure distributions, and, for comparison, some actual-flight pressure distributions of Crowley (Reference 41), showing the rearward shift that takes place at low angles of attack due to the above-noted shifts in centers of pressure. Note that since Cl_i is negative at angles below a, the effect of moving the aerodynamic center forward is actually to move the center of pressure farther to the rear. This effect can also be seen in the test results cited above, where the values of Cq are higher in proportion at the lower angles of attack.

The pitching moment resulting from the stabilizer section moment is by no means negligible but is dealt with separately in Appendix 2C.

C. Stabilizer Aerodynamics (1903)

The biplane stabilizers of all the Wright canards were constructed with thin, bendable ribs, connected by a control linkage that caused them to bend into a camber that increased with increasing stabilizer angle of incidence. A full-scale mockup of rib and control linkage was built, as shown in Figure 38, for the purpose of evaluating this camber/incidence relationship, from which it was learned that camber is 0 at $-9.88°$ incidence, and that it increases approximately linearly as follows:

$$Yh = .0028(Ah + 9.88)$$

Bending-moment analysis of the ribs gives y/Y as a function of x

$$yh/Yh = 2.157x^4 - 3.451x^3 - 2.588x^2 + 3.882x$$

$$yh/Yh = \qquad \text{when } x = .4763$$

These values are tabulated for Yh = .05 in Table 3 for 80 chord stations.

Thin-line values for ao are computed by the methods of Glauert and Pankhurst respectively, $-101.9Y$ and $-100.32Y$ so we write

$$-aoh = 100Yh = .28(Ah + 9.88)$$

Munk's 2-dimensional biplane lift factor for the stabilizer's g/c of .852 is B = .825 giving a biplane lift-curve slope of 1.65 = 5.18/rad. For the gap/span ratio of 26/144 Munk's EMS = $1.15b_h$ = 13.8

$$A = \frac{13.8^2}{52.75} = 3.6$$

and the shape of the Wright 1903 horizontal stabilizer is nearly enough elliptical that I have not applied any plan-form correction. So therefore

$$\frac{1}{S1} = \frac{1}{3.6} + \frac{1}{5.18} = .2815$$

$$S1 = 3.55 \qquad s1 = .062$$

Because of its variable camber the stabilizer will have an indefinite number of lift-coefficient curves. To plot realistic curves for simulation purposes, beginning with the uncambered section, presents certain difficulties because of the scarcity of empirical information concerning tests of sections of this configuration. Plotted in Figure 36 are the maximum lift coefficients of uncambered sections from the NACA 66-series (Reference 31). It can be seen that there is a decrease in maximum lift as the section thickness and the leading-edge radius are decreased. Theodorsen notes

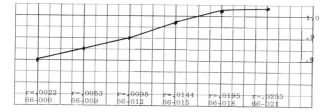

36. Lift maxima for uncambered NACA 66—airfoil sections.

that the "entrance losses" of wing sections are greater with decreasing leading-edge radius, but gives no quantitative information (Reference 26, p. 418).

Noting that the stabilizer section of the 1903 machine has a leading-edge spar 5/8" thick with corners rounded to 3/16" radius, the latter being .00239 chord, while the leading-edge radius of the 66-006 section is .00223, maximum-lift figures for that section are taken as a useful guide for estimating maximum stabilizer lift. Where the 2-dimensional lift for the 66-006 is .8, allowing for biplane effects and 3-dimensional losses, the uncambered stabilizer lift maximum has been taken to be 0.65. A curve has been plotted accordingly, as seen in Figure 36, with a family of lift curves for different cambers and their corresponding angles of incidence. Up to 16° this curve is represented by equation (Reference 5) in which p = 5, a_{max} = 13° and k = 4.34 × 10^{-7} sl = .062.

The leading-edge configuration suggests that under-wing burbles will be seen at all negative angles of attack. However, negative angles of attack are not encountered during steady-state flight configuration in which the cg is forward of the 36% station, so no effort has been made to find out what the effects of under-wing burbles might be.

Stabilizer downwash is partially neutralized by the fact that the stabilizer span is only 30% of the wing span, and since the wing will encounter the upwash from the attached vortices, the resultant downwash will be that of the bound vortex only. According to Millikan (Reference 33), the angle of downwash will be Clh/A = .09Clh. Tests by Silverstein, et al. (Reference 34) show that at 1.3 semi-spans behind the wing's quarter-chord point this angle is decreased about 20% from its original value, so that we take elevator downwash to be

$$\frac{w}{V} = .072Clh$$

Flying between 0 and 15 feet altitude, as the Wrights did, would reduce this to between 0 and .06.

Elevator downwash has the effect of reducing wing lift without substantially affecting stabilizer moment. This effect can be readily produced by a reduction in effective area, with a corresponding increase in stabilizer moment arm. This will approximate

$$dCl = Sl\frac{w}{V} = 3.61 \times .072 = .26Clh$$

Consequently a 26% reduction in effective stabilizer area, with a 35% increase in effective moment arm will reproduce this effect accurately in simulated flight.

The pitching-moment coefficient of the stabilizer section, integrated by the Glauert method is

$$C_{qh} = \frac{-1.3Y_h}{R} = .000374(A_h + 9.88)$$

Rather than conduct a complete lift-distribution analysis of the stabilizer mean-line, this amount has been reduced in the same proportion as the observed reduction in the calculated pitching-moment of the wing section, approximately .066/.97, so that the pitching-moment coefficient of the stabilizer section at zero lift has been taken to be

$$C = .00025(ih + 9.88)$$

The stabilizer geometry of the 1905 machine is like that of the 1903, but one difference between the 1905 machine and its 1907 successor is that on the 1907 model the pivot point of the control arm is moved forward of the line between the pivot points of the two surfaces and its length is increased proportionately so that the connecting links between the arm and the surfaces are nearly vertical in the normal position. This difference is easily seen in Figures 38 and 39, the latter of which displays the geometry of the 1907 stabilizer. The configuration is clear from the drawing, Figure 11, and in many of the photographs of the machine in flight, such as Figure 12. The basic dimensions are taken from a letter dated August 9, 1908, to Orville from Wilbur while he was in France (Reference 44).

D. Drag

Bettis and Culick (Reference 28), in their tests of a ⅙-scale model of the 1903 Flyer, have provided test information on total drag of that machine. Their drag figures are for the entire machine, including stabilizer, while the coefficients refer to the wing area alone. The drag data plotted in Figure 33 is for the machine without stabilizer, since for simulation purposes it is necessary to carry the stabilizer drag as a separate component of the total, because of its variability with differing values of ih. The ratio of stabilizer drag to

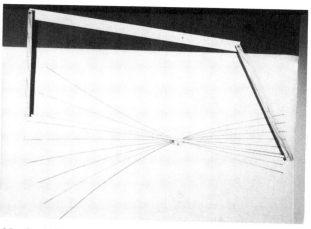
38. Stabilizer geometry, 1903 Flyer.

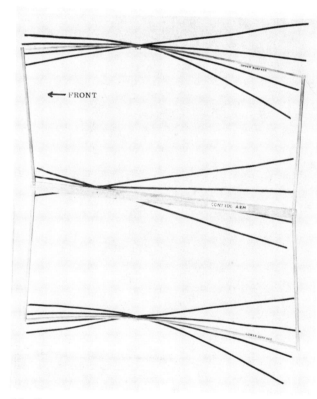
39. Stabilizer geometry, 1907 Flyer.

the total has been taken as equal to the ratio of its surface area to the total, which is .103 so the drag coefficients of Bettis and Culick run #1, taken with ih = 0, have been multiplied by .897 to obtain the drag for the machine without stabilizer.

Stabilizer drag is then reckoned for its unique angle of attack, using the same tables as tabulated for the rest of the machine, but multiplied by the ratio of stabilizer area to wing area. This method, while it is an approximation, gives results that are satisfactorily close to those given by Bettis and Culick for ih = 10, 7½ and 15, as well as those computed by more

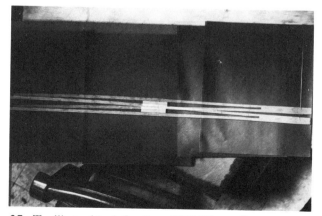
37. Trailing-edge deflection, 1903 Flyer rib.

exact assumptions concerning stabilizer profile and induced drag.

Drag has a significant effect on longitudinal statics in the 1903 Flyer, because it is relatively large in proportion to other aerodynamic forces, and because the thrust axis is high enough above the cg that thrust forces result in a significant pitching moment. Stabilizer drag also has a pitching-moment component at high and low angles of attack.

Bettis and Culick drag measurements are significantly higher than the Wrights estimated drag. In their notebook K (Reference 35) the Wrights' estimate was 90 lb, but this was at an estimated forward speed of 24 mph. At the Flyer's historic speed of 30 mph (44 fps), the drag according to Bettis and Culick would be 125 lb and, according to the Wrights' implied drag coefficient, it would be 140 lb. The Wrights had based this early estimate on an estimated weight of 630 lb and raised it to 100 lb when they realized that the weight would be over 700 lb (see Reference 24). They regarded 100 lb as very conservative, and were reassured by their measurement of 132 lb static thrust after the machine was assembled. Consequently, the machine requires 13.8 hp for level flight at 30 mph (44 fps) which means that their engine must have turned out more horsepower than the Wrights' tests had shown.

The required modifications of historically accepted numbers for engine power and propeller efficiency can be made without difficulty. Four factors must be taken in account: (1) Engine power, with cooler air of higher density, would be higher than static tests indicated; (2) engine cooling, on a cold day in flight, would be much more effective than in static tests, and the engine's output was highly dependent on cooling, because of the unjacketed valve cages and cylinder heads, as witness the decline in power as the engine warms up (see Reference 26); (3) induced drag was less than wind-tunnel measurements because of ground effects at the very low altitudes at which the flights took place; and (4) propeller efficiency was obviously higher than the Wrights' estimate of 66%, which included an exaggerated transmission loss as the result of Chanute's misinformation (see Reference 24) to the effect that chain losses would be 25–30%. The Wrights figured 10–15%, while the true losses were probably closer to 5%.

Drag for high angles of attack has been estimated from the data of Knight and Wentzinger (Reference 27).

APPENDIX 3

Longitudinal Statics and Dynamics

The mechanics of simulated flight will be presented in the way they are processed in the computer.

Aircraft measurements are given as follows for the 1903 Flyer, x coordinates given in units of c/100 from wing leading edge rearward, z coordinates from the cg upward.

1. $R = 9.67$ (Ratio of wing to stabilizer surface areas)
2. $D1 = -112$ (Distance, stabilizer 1/3 chord to wing leading edge)
3. $Wt = 750$ (Weight)
4. $Im = 280$ (Longitudinal moment of inertia, sl ft^2)
5. $S = 510$ (Wing surface area)
6. $ch = 6.5$ (Wing chord, ft)
7. $z1 = +23$ (Vertical coordinate of thrust vector upward from cg)
8. $z2 = +12$ (Vertical coordinate of drag center)
9. $z3 = +15$ (Vertical coordinate of lift center)
10. $zh = (cg + D1) \sin ap$ (Vertical coordinate of center of stabilizer drag)
11. $Fd = .00125$ (Density of air, sl/ft^3 at 40°F)

Flight conditions supplied by the operator for each flight: aa, angle of attack, Z, altitude.

The data bank is available that consists of a complete matrix of four flight coefficients for all angles from $-19°$ to $+30°$ angle of attack, Cl, Clh, Cd, and Cm (see Table 5).

The static conditions for equilibrium in level flight are set up according to the specified flight conditions in a "takeoff" routine. If equilibrium is not possible under the conditions specified the flight terminates with NO TAKEOFF.

The process flight variables are set up as follows:

The specified angle of attack is divided into integral and fractional parts for data look up and interpolation to establish flight variables. Cl, Cd, and Cm are then looked up for the specified angle of attack and C is computed

$$C = Cm - Cl(Cg - z1 \sin a_p)$$

To establish equilibrium stabilizer angle, the range of angles is scanned by 1° increments as Kh is looked up for that angle and corrected for camber according to incidence setting.

$$Kh - Kl = .017 J/R$$

Kl is looked up as a function of $I + J$. When the total positive moment exceeds the total negative moment, the scan goes back a degree and then advances by increments of .01° until equilibrium is reached when

$$(Dl + Cg)(Kh + Kd \sin (AP)$$
$$= C + .25J/R + Kdz2 + Cd(z2 - z3)$$

After the stabilizer scan the following variables are computed:

$$B = J + J2$$

$$V = 2\,Wt\,(Cl + Kh)/Pd^{1/2}$$

$$Th = V^2\,pd(Cd + Kd)$$

$$H = Vth/400$$

The takeoff routine is completed by a printout of the flight variable headings and a list of the variables as they exist at takeoff

$$T \quad V_v \quad z \quad aa \quad ap \quad af \quad w \quad P \quad V \quad B-10$$

Flight data is listed in the same columns during the flight routine.

Figure 40 is a force vector diagram of the 1903 Flyer, and Figure 14 is a plot of all possible values of stabilizer incidence vs. angle of attack for equilibrium over a range of cg positions from 8 to 35. Regions of positive slope are regions of stable flight.

The flight routine begins with the listing of the various optional subroutines, for automatic landing, automatic pilot, random wind gusts. Then the stabilizer angle is corrected for pitch motion

$$Be = B - 57.3\,TAN^{-1}\,(Dl + Cg)\,ch/100\,w/V$$

The following functions are updated by look up, Cd, Cm, Kh, Kd, Cl

then $Pd = V^2 Sda/2$

$$L = Pd(Cl + Kh)$$

$$Dg = Pd(Cd + Kd)$$

$$C = Cm - Cl(Cg - zl\sin(Ap))$$

$$af = \frac{gt(L - Wt\cos(af))}{WtV}$$

$$\begin{aligned}P = ch/100\,(&-z2\,Th + Pd\,(Cd\,z3 - C\\ &+ Kh\,(Dl + Cg) + Kd\sin(Ap)))\end{aligned}$$

$$W = W + \frac{P}{T\,Im}$$

$$Ap = Ap + WT$$

$$Aa = Ap + Ai - Af$$

$$Th = 400\,H/V$$

$$V = V + gT\,[(Th - Dg)/Wt - \sin(Af)]$$

$$Vv = V\sin Af$$

$$Z = Z + VvT$$

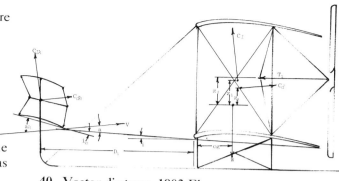

40. Vector diagram, 1903 Flyer.

APPENDIX 4

The Simulation Program

The preceding discussion shows the nature of the processing of the program, basically a straightforward interaction of static equations.

The program is listed in Appendix 1, and is annotated for those who wish to follow it in detail. Its nomenclature is the same as that of the present discussion.

These two flight routines take up pages 3 and 4 of 8, of which 1 is nomenclature, 2 is data assembly, 5 is landing and printout routines, 6 is devoted to control options, 7 to subroutines and 8 to data.

The operator, who specifies cg location, angle of attack, and altitude before the flight takes off, controls stabilizer incidence and throttle, although manual stabilizer control is not possible in unstable flight regimes. Throttle is specified in terms of power. Any amount of power is available. For unstable flight an automatic pilot is necessary. Its reaction time is controllable between 0 and .08 seconds, and its sensitivity can also be adjusted.

As page 6 of the program will show, there are many options available to the operator who may vary the frequency of printouts and pauses for instructions, to begin and end wind-gust routines, to activate automatic pilots and lander, or to eliminate further instructions.

```
1000! SIMULATING THE FLIGHT OF THE 1903 WRIGHT FLYER---BY F.J. HOOVEN
1020!    Aircraft dimensions are measured along longitudinal axis
1040!    in units of percent wingchord from leading edge rearward.
1060!    All motion is in the vertical longitudinal plane.
1080!
1100!    NOMENCLATURE
1120!
1140!    Ai,Aa,Ap,Af = Angles of incidence, attack, pitch and path, radians
1160!    B = Elevator-to-wing angle, degrees + 10
1180!    B1 = Effective angle of elevator as corrected for pitch motion
1200!    B3 = Automatic pilot time-delay index
1220!    C = Pitching-moment coefficient about center of gravity
1240!    Cg = Position coordinate of airplane center of gravity, percent chord
1260!    ch = Wing chord, feet
1280!    Cm = Pitching-moment coefficient
1300!    Cd = Drag coefficient for complete aircraft except elevator
1320!    Dg = Total drag of airplane less stabilizer, pounds
1340!    DL = Distance from leading edge to aerodynamic center of elevator
1360!    F(I), B3 = Pilot-reaction-time factors
1380!    Fd = One half density of air times wing surface area
1400!    K1,K(I) = Elevator lift coefficient as applied and as tabulated
1420!    GV,V9 = Velocity values for random wind gusts
1440!    H = Horsepower at engine shaft, assuming propulsion efficiency of 72.7%
1460!    I,I2 = Angle of attack integral degrees + 10 and hundredths
1480!    Im = Aircraft moment of inertia, slug-feet squared
1500!    J,J2 = Elevator angle integral degrees + 10 and hundredths
1520!    Kh = Lift coefficient of elevator corrected for variable camber
1540!    Kd, E(J) = Drag coefficient of stabilizer
1560!    Kl,K(I) = Elevator lift coefficient
1580!    Lz = Lift of wing and elevator, pounds
1600!    M1---Mn = Flag variables
1620!    N = Time increment count
1640!    P = Pitching moment
1660!    Pd = Dynamic pressure, lbs/sq.ft.
1680!    Q = Input variable for instructions
1700!    Q1, Q2, Q3 = Angle-of-attack, sensitivity and flag for automatic pilot
1720!    Q4 = Autopilot damping factor
1740!    R = Ratio of wing area to elevator area
1760!    S = Wing surface area, square feet
1780!    T = Finite time increment, seconds
1800!    Th = Thrust, pounds
1820!    T8,T9 = Random-wind gust duration, seconds
1840!    U,U1 = Integral and fractional angle of attack of elevator
1860!    V = Airspeed, ft/sec
1880!    Vv = Vertical velocity
1900!    W = Rate of change of pitch angle
1920!    Wt = Weight of aircraft, pounds
1940!    X1 = Horizontal distance flown, feet
1960!    Z = Altitude, feet
1980!    Z1,Z2,Z3 = Vertical coordinates of center of life, drag and thrust
2000!    THIS PROGRAM IS WRITTEN IN DARTMOUTH BASIC7
2040!    In the following routine the specifications and aerodynamics
2060!    of the Flyer are read into the program.
2100  PRINT "SIMULATED FLIGHT OF THE 1903 WRIGHT FLYER"
2120  LET R = 9.7 (Dimensions of the Flyer are given)
2140  LET DL = 112
2160  LET Wt = 750
2180  LET Im = 280
2200  LET S = 510
2220  LET ch = 6.5
2260  LET Z1 = 15
2280  LET Z2 = 23
2300  LET Z3 = 13
2320  LET Cg = 29
2340  LET Q2,Q4 = 1.5 (Autopilot settings)
2360  LET B7 = 2
2380  LET B3 = 3
```

```
2440   LET Ai = 8/57.3 (Angle of incidence)
2480!   In this section the aerodynamic data is read out of the data bank
2500!   and certain variables are given initial values.
2540   DIM D(110),E(110),F(10),G(110),K(110),L(110),M(110)
2560   FOR I = 1 TO 90 (Lift coefficients)
2580     IF I<41 THEN 2640
2600     LET Lz = 720 − 8*I (This algorithm for approximate coefficients from 30--80°)
2620     GO TO 2660
2640     READ Lz
2660     LET L(I) = Lz/1000
2680   NEXT I
2700   FOR I = 1 TO 110 (Stabilizer Lift)
2710     IF I<51 THEN 2740
2720     LET K1 = 550 − 5*I
2730     GO TO 2750
2740     READ K1
2750     LET K(I) = K1/1000/R
2760   NEXT I
2770   FOR I = 1 to 110 (Drag coefficients)
2780     IF I<51 THEN 2810
2790     LET Cd = 50 + 10*I
2800     GO TO 2820
2810     READ Cd
2820     LET D(I) = Cd/1000
2830   NEXT I
2840   FOR I = 1 to 90 (Pitching-moment coefficients)
2850     IF I<41 THEN 2880
2860     LET Cm = 140 + 4*I
2870     GO TO 2890
2880     READ Cm
2890     LET M(I) = Cm/10
2900   NEXT I
2910   LET T = .02 (The time period of iteration)
2920   LET Fd = .00125*S (1/2 density of air and wing surface area)
2940   LET Af,M4,M6,M7,M8,M9,N,N9,Q1,Q3,Vv,W,X1 = 0 (Reset for a new flight)
2960   RESTORE
2970   PRINT "Z,Aa";
2980   INPUT Z,Aa (Operator inputs altitude and angle of attack)
2990   LET Q1 = Aa (This sets the automatic pilot target angle)
3000!   Next is the takeoff routine in which are established the variables
3020!   for steady-state flight under the conditions specified in the data input.
3040   FOR I = 1 TO B3 (Reset the time-lag loop for the autopilot)
3048     LET F(I) = 0
3054   NEXT I
3060   LET I = INT(Aa) + 10 (Set the data matrix in line with the angle of attack
3080   LET I2 = Aa + 10 − I       including the fractional value for interpolation)
3100   LET Cl = L(I) + I2*(L(I + 1) − L(I)) (Look up and interpolate for lift coefficient)
3120   LET Aa = Aa/57.3 (Change angle of attack to radians)
3140   LET Cd = D(I + 10) + I2*(D(I + 11) − D(I + 10)) (Lookup and interpolate for drag coefficient)
3160   LET Cm = M(I) + I2*(M(I + 1) − M(I)) (Lookup and interpolate for pitching-moment coefficient)
3180   LET Ap = Aa − Ai (Set pitch angle for level flight)
3200   LET C = Cm − Cl*(Cg − Zl*SIN(Ap)) (Compute C including "pendulum" pitch moment)
3220   PRINT "C = ";C,
3230!
3240   FOR J = 1 TO 37 − I (Scan the range of stabilizer angles)
3280     LET K(J) = K(I + J) + I2*(K(I + J + 1) − K(I + J)) + .17*J/R (lookup stabilizer lift and for stabilizer drag)
3300     LET E(J) = (D(I + J) + I2*(D(I + J + 1) − D(I + J)))/R
3320     IF (DL + Cg)*(K(J) + E(J)*SIN(Ap))>C + .25*J/R + E(J)*Z2 + Cd*(Z2 − Z3) THEN 3480
3400   NEXT J (When the stabilizer lift equals the pitch moment equilibrium has arrived)
3420   PRINT "NO TAKEOFF" (If the lift is not enough the flight terminates)
3440   GO TO 2940
3460!
3480   LET J = J − 1 (Set the angle back 1 and scan .01 degree at a time)
3500!
3520   FOR J2 = 0 TO .99 STEP .01
3540     LET Kh = K(J) + J2*(K(J + 1) − K(J))
3560     LET Kd = E(J) + J2*(E(J + 1) − E(J))
```

```
3580      IF (DL+Cg)*(Kh+Kd*SIN(Ap))>C+.25*(J+J2)/R+Kd*Z2+Cd*(Z2−Z3) THEN 3640
3600    NEXT J2
3620!
3640    LET B=J+J2
3720    LET V,Vh=SQR(Wt/Fd/(Cl+Kh)) (There are separate Vs for stabilizer and wing for gusts)
3760    LET Th=V*V*Fd*(Cd+Kd)
3780    PRINT "V=";V,
3800    LET H=Th*V/400
3820    PRINT INT (100*H)/100,
3840    LET M1=1 (This is the "in flight" flag)
3860    PRINT "T      Vv      Z      Aa      Ap      Af      W      X1      V      B"
3880      LET Pd=V*V*Fd (Print out flight data headings)
3940    GO TO 5600 (Go to print routine to print out initial flight variables)
3980    PRINT
3990    LET V5=V4 (This is part of a routine for flagging when Vv goes through
3999    LET V4=Vv        zero, through a maximum, or through a minimum)
4000!      This is the Regular Flight Routine.
4020    IF Q3=1 THEN 7420 (Flag for the automatic-landing subroutine)
4040    IF M6=0 THEN 4100 (If it is up the landing begins when we are 1 1/2
4060    IF −Vv>2*Z/3 THEN 7360        seconds from ground)
4100    IF N9=0 THEN 4140 (Flag for the random-wind-gust subroutine)
4120    IF N=>T9 THEN 7820 (If it is up we wait for the gust duration to end)
4140    IF Q1<>0 THEN 7525 (Flag for the automatic-pilot subroutine)
4180    LET B1=B−57.3*ATN((DL+Cg)*ch/100*W/V) (Correct stabilizer angle for pitch motion)
4200    LET I=INT(57.3*Aa)+10 (Set matrix to angle of attack)
4220    LET I2=57.3*Aa+10−I
4240    LET U=INT(I+I2+B1) (Also to stabilizer angle of attack)
4260    LET U1=I+I2+B1−U
4300    LET Cd=D(I+10)+I2*(D(I+11)−D(I+10)) (Lookup for drag coefficient)
4310    LET Cm=M(I)+I2*(M(I+1)−M(I)) (Pitching-moment coefficient)
4320    LET Kh=K(U)+U1*(K(U+1)−K(U))+.017*B/R (Stabilizer lift)
4330    LET Kd=(D(U)+U1*(D(U+1)−D(U)))/R (Stabilizer drag)
4340    LET Cl=L(I)+I2*(L(I+1)−L(I)) (Lift coefficient)
4342    IF N<>T7 THEN 4350 (Time a wind gust from stabilizer to wing)
4344    LET V=V+V9*N9 (Change airspeed by the amount of the gust)
4350    LET Pd=V*V*Fd (Dynamic pressure at wing)
4355    LET Ph=Vh*Vh*Fd (Dynamic pressure at stabilizer)
4360    LET Lz=Cl*Pd+Kh*Ph (Compute lift force and drag force)
4380    LET Dg=Cd*Pd+Kd*Ph
4400    LET C=Cm−Cl*(Cg−Zl*SIN(Ap))+.25*B/R (Pitching moment coefficient about cg)
4420    LET Af=Af+T*32*(Lz−Wt*COS(Af))/Wt/V (Correct flight path by applied forces)
4440    LET P=ch/100*(−Z2*Th+Pd*(Cd*Z3−C)+Ph*((DL+Cg)*Kh+Kd*SIN(Ap))) (Pitching moment)
4460    LET W=W+P/Im*T (Pitching-motion angular velocity)
4480    LET Ap=Ap+W*T (Pitching angle updated)
4500    LET Aa=Ap+Ai−Af (Angle of attack updated)
4520    IF Aa*57.3<50 THEN 4580
4540    PRINT "STALL"
4560    GO TO 5260
4580    IF Aa*57.3>−7 THEN 4620
4600    PRINT "EXCESSIVE NEGATIVE LIFT"
4610    GO TO 5160
4620    IF U+U1<110 THEN 4650
4630    PRINT "ELEVATOR STALL, U+U1=";U+U1
4640    GO TO 5160
4650    IF U+U1>2 THEN 4680
4655    PRINT "EXCESS NEGATIVE ELEVATOR, U+U1=";U+U1
4660    GO TO 5160
4680    LET Th=400*H/V (Compute thrust)
4720    LET DV=32*T*(SIN(Af)+(Dg−Th)/Wt) (Update velocity)
4730    LET V=V−DV
4740    LET Vh=Vh−DV
4760    LET X1=X1+V*T*COS(Af) (Update horizontal distance flown)
4840    LET Vv=V*SIN(Ap) (Compute vertical velocity)
4860    LET Z=Z+Vv*T (Update altitude)
4880    LET N=N+1 (Keep track of time)
4960    IF Z>0 THEN 5480 (If there is still altitude, continue flight with printout decision.)
5000!    This is the landing routine
```

```
5020!   If the rate of descent is less than 6 ft/sec when the
5040!   aircraft reaches the ground, it's a good landing.
5060!   If it's between 6 and 10 ft/sec it's a hard landing.
5080!   If it's more than 10 it's a crash.
5100!
5120    IF Vv>-8 THEN 5200
5140    IF Vv>-12 THEN 5240
5160    PRINT "Crash at";
5180    GO TO 5260
5200    PRINT "Land at";
5260    LET M1=0
5280    PRINT N*T; "Sec"
5290    LET X=X+V*(INT(N/50)+1-N/50)
5300    GO TO 5600
5310!
5320!       This is the printout routine.
5340!       Printout normally takes place one per second of flight time.
5360!       Printout also takes place at maximum and minimum values of the
5380!       vertical velocity, Vv.
5440!       By means of special instructions printout may be caused to
5460!       take place at shorter intervals.
5470!
5480    IF V4*Vv*(V4-V5)*(V4-Vv)>0 THEN 5600 (Prints if Vu goes through zero, maximum or minimum)
5500    IF M8>N THEN 5600       (Flag for 1/50th-second printout)
5520    IF INT(N/5)<N/5 THEN 3990     (Sieve for 1/10th-second printout)
5540    IF M9>N THEN 5600 (Flag for 1/10th-second printout)
5560    IF ABS(W)>20/57.3 THEN 5600 (If pitching motion gets over 20°/sec, print each 1/10th sec.)
5580    IF INT(N/50)<N/50 THEN 3990 (Sieve for 1-second printout)
5600!
5620    PRINT N*T;TAB(7);
5640    PRINT INT(100*Vv+.5)/100;TAB(14);
5645    IF Z<50 THEN 5660
5650    PRINT INT(Z+.5);TAB(21);
5655    GO TO 5680
5660    PRINT INT(100*Z+.5)/100;TAB(21);
5680    PRINT .01* INT(5730*Aa.5);TAB(28);
5700    PRINT .1*INT(573*Ap-.5-10*Ai);TAB(35);
5720    PRINT INT(573*Af)/10;TAB(42);
5740    PRINT INT(5730*W+.5)/100;TAB(49);
5760    PRINT INT(X1);
5780    PRINT TAB(55);
5800    PRINT INT(10*V+.5)/10;
5820    PRINT TAB(62);
5860    PRINT INT(100*(B-10)+.5/100;
5880    PRINT INT(100*F(B3))'
5960    IF M1=1 THEN 6200 (If the "in flight" flag is still up go on with the flight)
5980    GO TO 2940
6000!   This section contains the routines for special instructions.
6020!   Normally the program will ask for instructions one per second
6040!   at the time of printout. This may, at option, be changed to occur
6060!   ten times per second, once every ten seconds, or not at all.
6080!
6100!   In-flight changes can be made in elevator angle and throttle setting; in
6120!   windspeed for simulating wind gusts. An angle of attack can be entered
6140!   that will activate the autopilot, causing it to control the elevator
6160!   to maintain that angle. An automatic landing sequence may be activated.
6180!
6200    IF INT(N/5)<N/5 THEN 3980 (These are sieves for 1/10th and 1 second instruction pauses)
6220    IF M7>N THEN 6320 (Flag for .1 second instruction interval)
6240    IF INT(N/50)<(N/50) THEN 3980
6260    IF M4=2 THEN 3980 (Flag for no instructions at all)
6280    IF N<M4 THEN 3980
6300!
6320    INPUT Q
6360    IF Q>499 THEN 6800! Enter 500 + 10*Q1, the autopilot angle of attack
6380    IF Q>299 THEN 7180! ENTERS 300 plus a time without further instructions
6400    IF Q>99 THEN 6740! Enter 100 plus desired horsepower
```

```
6420   IF Q<23 THEN 6660! Numbers less than 22 command elevator angles
6440   IF Q=23 THEN 7100! 23 activates the landing system
6480   IF Q=24 THEN 6700! Complete the flight without further instructions
6500   IF Q=25 THEN 6940! Gives .1 sec instruction pause, with printout
6520   IF Q=26 THEN 7020! Print out every 1/50 second for 1 second
6540   IF Q=27 THEN 7060! Print out every .1 second for 1 second
6560   IF Q=28 THEN 6900! Print out and instructions each second
6580   IF Q=29 THEN 5980! 29 signals to terminate the flight
6600   IF Q=30 THEN 6960! Q=30 Cancels the wind-gust routine
6620   IF Q>30 THEN 6840! Enter 30 + random wind-gust velocity
6660   LET B=Q+10! −10<Q<23 calls for an elevator setting
6680   GO TO 7200
6700   LET M4=2
6720   GO TO 7200
6740   LET H=Q−100
6750   GO TO 7200
6800   LET Q1=.1*(Q−500)
6820   GO TO 7200
6840   LET N9=1
6860   LET GV=Q−30
6880   GO TO 7200
6900   LET M4,M7,M8,M9=0
6920   GO TO 7200
6940   LET M7,M9=49+N
6960   LET N9=0
6980   GO TO 3990
6990!
6995!
6996!
6999!
7000   GO TO 7200
7020   LET M8=N+50
7040   GO TO 7200
7060   LET M9=N+50
7080   GO TO 7200
7100   LET M6=1
7120   GO TO 7200
7180   LET M4=50*(Q−300)+N
7200   IF INT(100*Q+.1)/10=INT(10*Q+.01) THEN 3990
7220   LET Q=INT(10*Q)/10
7240   GO TO 6300
7320!   The final section of the program contains the various subroutines
7340!   The landing subroutine follows
7360   LET Q3=1
7370   LET Q2,Q4=2 (Sharpen up the autopilot for the landing)
7380   PRINT "LANDING BEGINS"
7420   LET B3=1
7520   LET Q1=6+V/20−.1*Z−.1*Vv (Set the landing speed target)
7525!   The autopilot routine follows
7528   IF ABS(Q1−57.3*Aa)>1 THEN 7535 (This is 1--degree offset for angle of
                                        attack response)
7530   LET F(B3)=1.5*Q2*(Q1/57.3−Aa/2−(Ai+Ap)/2)
7532   GO TO 7538
7535   LET F(B3)=1.5*Q2*(Q1/57−Aa)
7538   IF ABS(W)<.01*B7 THEN 7544 (This is offset for pitch-damping response)
7540   LET F(B3)=F(B3)−1.5*Q4*2−.00014*P
7544   FOR I=1 TO B3−1 (This is the time-lag loop)
7548   LET F(I)=F(I+1)
7552   NEXT I
7556   LET B=B+F(1) (The autopilot updates the stabilizer control)
7580   IF U+U1<35 THEN 7640 (Don't move the control past the stall point)
7600   IF Q2*F(B3)<0 THEN 7640
7620   LET F(B3)=0
7640!
7660   IF U+U1>10 THEN 7720 (Or into a negative-lift situation)
7680   IF Q2*F(B3)>0 THEN 7720
7700   LET F(B3)=0
```

Frederick J. Hooven

```
7720    GO TO 4180
7820!    The random-wind subroutine follows
7830    LET Vh = V (The maximum gust speed is specified)
7840    IF N9<0 THEN 7900
7860    LET V9 = RND*(GV−0) (Gust speed is random amount up to that maximum)
7865    LET GA = RND*(GV/500−0)
7870    LET A5 = A5 + GA*N9
7880    LET T8 = INT(RND*(150−20)) + N (Gust timing is random up to 3 seconds)
7900    LET Vh = Vh + V9*N9
7920    LET T7 = INT(450/Vh) + N (Times the gust from stabilizer to wing)
7940    LET N9 = −N9
7960    RANDOMIZE
7970    LET T9 = T8 + N
7980    GO TO 4140
8000!    The aerodynamic data bank follows
8020!
8160!    L(I)   Wing lift coefficients in absolute units *1000
8180!
8200    DATA −270,−248,−208,−168,−128,−88,52,142,225,300!   −9,0
8220    DATA 367,430,493,556,618,680,740,800,857,912!   1,10
8240    DATA 963,1010,1050,1082,1103,1110,1110,1072,1017,932!   11,20
8260    DATA 810,760,730,700,700,700,700,700,705,710!   21,30
8280!
8300!    K(I) Lift coefficients of elevator section without camber
8320!
8340    DATA −500,−500,−500,−528,−590,−624,−634,−624,−602,−567!   −19,−10
8360    DATA −523,−474,−419,−363,−304,−244,−183,−122,−61,0!   −9,0
8380    DATA 61,122,183,244,304,363,419,474,523,567!   1,10
8400    DATA 602,625,634,624,590,528,510,500,500,500!   10,20
8420    DATA 490,460,440,420,400,380,360,340,320,300!   21,30
8440!
8460!    D(I) Coefficients of drag for total aircraft less elevator
8480!
8500    DATA 387,376,353,332,301,272,245,217,190,168!   −19,−10
8520    DATA 152,136,122,109,100,91,84,77,75,73!   −9,0
8540    DATA 75,80,84,91,100,109,122,136,152,168!   1,10
8560    DATA 190,217,245,272,301,331,353,376,387,399!   11,20
8580    DATA 415,430,443,457,468,480,493,507,518,530!   21,30
8600!
8620!    M, Pitching-moment coefficients
8640!
8660    DATA 34,34,34,34,34,54,72,101,127,148!   −9,0
8680    DATA 165,180,195,210,224,239,254,269,284,299!   1,10
8700    DATA 313,328,337,344,350,353,350,345,338,334!   11,20
8720    DATA 319,308,297,286,286,286,286,286,286,286!   21,30
8800!
99999   END
```

Propulsion Systems of the Wright Brothers

HARVEY H. LIPPINCOTT

Introduction

Everything concerning the Wright brothers and their achievements has been said before, by the Wrights themselves and by later students of their work. Consequently, this paper affords a summary of the Wrights' propulsion work that was so essential for the successful flight of their airplanes. The reader interested in an expanded knowledge of the Wrights' propulsion systems should consult References 1 through 4.

From their earliest investigations, the Wright brothers thought in terms of powered flight. But first they realized that the key elements of aircraft control and configuration had to be determined and demonstrated. As practical engineers, they chose to pursue their work in a step-by-step procedure, using gliders without the complication of a propulsion system. By the end of 1902, they had solved the problem of flight control, had determined a practical basic configuration for the airplane, and had acquired enough actual flight experience to feel comfortable in handling a powered machine. In the meanwhile they collected information on propellers and engines and thought seriously upon the matter.

To propel their airplanes through the air, the Wrights knew that they had to have thrust. They had to develop a propulsion system. In those days thrust was produced by a propeller. In order to produce thrust, the propeller required energy to turn it. To develop energy, an engine was required. However, to run the engine properly, a support system was needed to supply fuel, oil, and cooling water. All three systems—thrust, energy, and support—were required to provide propulsion. Lacking any one, nothing would happen. As elements of these systems were not readily available, the Wrights had to develop all three.

Probably the most difficult of the three to develop was the propeller. At that time the Wrights had no real understanding of the air propeller—how it worked, how it should be designed. There was no valid propeller theory in their knowledge.

Frank W. Caldwell, the eminent propeller designer, pointed out that

> Some time before any actual flights in airplanes, a theory of the air propeller was evolved more or less independently by Lanchester, Drzweiecke, and Prandtl in Germany. This theory is based on the conception of the airplane propeller as a series of wing sections moving in a spiral path. Knowing the characteristics of these wing sections, it was possible to predict the performance of the propeller by means of mathematical calculations. It is interesting that the Wright brothers evolved this theory independently without knowledge of the work of the earlier scientists.[1]

The problem facing the Wrights, to design a suitable and efficient propeller, was amply stated by them in an article in *The Century Magazine*, September 1908:

> Our table made the designing of the wings an easy matter; and as screw propellers are simply wings traveling in a spiral course, we anticipated no trouble from this source. We had thought of getting the theory of the screw propeller from the marine engineers, and then, by applying our tables of air pressure to their formulas, of designing air propellers suitable for our purpose. But so far as we could learn,

the marine engineers possessed only empirical formulas, and the exact action of the screw propeller, after a century of use, was still very obscure.[2]

Further, Orville Wright gave a graphic description of the perplexing problem they had to solve:

It was apparent that a propeller was simply an aeroplane (aerofoil) traveling in a spiral course. As we could calculate the effect of an aeroplane traveling in a straight course, why should we not be able to calculate the effect of one traveling in a spiral course? At first glance this does not appear difficult, but on further consideration it is hard to find even a point from which to make a start; for nothing about a propeller, or the medium in which it acts, stands still for a moment. The thrust depends upon the speed and the angle at which the blade strikes the air; the angle at which the blade strikes the air depends upon the speed at which the propeller is turning, the speed the machine is traveling forward, and the speed at which the air is slipping backward; the slip of the air backward depends upon the thrust exerted by the propeller, and the amount of air acted upon. When any of these changes, it changes all the rest, as they are all interdependent upon one another. But these are only a few of the many factors that must be considered and determined in calculating and designing propellers.[3]

To solve this problem, the Wrights rejected a long series of experiments to devise a suitable propeller by trial-and-error methods as too costly in time. They elected to develop a theory from which they could calculate the propeller performance and dimensions. The Wrights became so obsessed with the problem that they spent long hours in study and debate to develop an understanding of the complex subject. By February 1903, they had progressed to the point where the first full-sized propeller was made and statically tested. The propeller had a diameter of 8½ feet, a blade width of 6 inches, pitch of 15 degrees, and gave 18¾ pounds of thrust at 245 revolutions per minute. Afterward they came to realize that "the thrust generated by a propeller when standing stationary was no indication of the thrust when in motion."[4]

Their propeller theory emerged gradually with their formulae improving with experience. Unfortunately, the Wrights never organized their theory in a logically written form that others could understand. What is known is extracted from various entries of formulae, test results, and tables scattered among their many notebooks. Using these sources, McFarland, in Appendix III of *The Papers of Wilbur and Orville Wright*, assembled as good a review as possible of their theory.

From their propeller performance diagrams, the Wrights developed formulae for thrust, torque, slip, blade width of an ideal screw, and others. Using the formulae, they then developed tables of quantities from which they could choose the propeller characteristics to fulfill their needs.

Modern propeller theory is based upon two theories: the blade-element theory and the momentum theory. The two theories complement each other. The theory developed by the Wrights combined features of both theories.[5]

At first, and through 1904, the blade element used was an arc. Wright aerofoil no. 9 was the most efficient arc tested in the wind tunnel experiments and undoubtedly was the surface employed. In 1905 the propellers were redesigned to produce greater thrust and efficiency and given a new shape. The blade element in the redesigned propeller was a parabolic curve of Wright aerofoil no. 12. While these profiles were not very efficient for low incidence, they were quite good for high angles and, consequently, good for take-off.

On the application of their propeller to the airplane, the Wrights made three basic decisions:

1. Two propellers would be used, each absorbing half the power of the engine and producing half the needed thrust. Two propellers would give a reaction against a greater quantity of air with larger pitch angle than was possible with a single propeller. Consequently, the propeller rotational speed could be lower.

2. The propellers, to eliminate torque effects upon control of the airplane, would turn in opposite directions, thereby cancelling the torque effect of each propeller.

3. The propellers would be mounted at the rear of the wings as pushers to eliminate the effect upon the wings of turbulent airflow over them from tractor propellers.

Another important decision had to be made: how to drive the propellers. Little was known of desirable or limiting speed ratios between engines and propeller. Should it be a direct-driven single propeller attached to the engine's crankshaft? Or, should it be remotely mounted propellers driven indirectly by the engine? The direct-driven propeller offered no flexibility to vary experimentally engine and propeller speed ratios while providing an undersirable out-of-balance torque force to the control of the airplane.

Two methods of driving remotely mounted propellers were available: (1) drive-shafting with gears or (2) systems of chains or belts. The first would be inflexible, heavy, and costly, requiring new gears for each experimental change in the search for optimum engine/propeller speed ratio. The latter would permit a simple, inexpensive flexible range of speed ratios. Chain-drive systems were, at that time, frequently used in automobiles and other machinery and were readily available in a wide range of sizes. The Wrights had experience with chain-driven bicycles and chose to employ a chain drive with their propellers. Hence, a flywheel and chain sprockets were incorporated on the engine for the propeller drive. Power loss in the transmission system was estimated to be 5 percent (Figure 1).

1. Propulsion system installed in 1903 airplane with engine mounted on lower wing and chain drive to strut-mounted propellers. (SI neg. A38388)

However, the chain drive was not without its problems. As Leonard S. Hobbs pointed out:

> Torque variations in the engine would tend to cause a whipping action in the chain, so that it was vulnerable to rough running caused by misfiring cylinders and, with the right timing and magnitude of normal regular variations, the action could result in destructive forces in the transmission system. This was the basic reason for the Wrights' great fear of "engine vibration," which confined them to the use of small cylinders and made a fairly heavy flywheel necessary on all their engines.[6]

The Wrights had progressed in their propeller work so that by June 1903 they had made their first flight propellers which were made of three 1⅛-inch laminations of spruce, glued together. The propellers were shaped by hatchet and drawshave. Tips were covered with canvas and were 8½ feet in diameter and 8 inches in width, pitch 27 degrees, and had a blade area of 5.4 square feet. At an airplane speed of 24 miles per hour and turning at 330 revolutions per minute the two propellers were designed to give a combined thrust of 90 pounds. Tip speed was 180 feet/second. Efficiency was 66 percent. Sprocket ratio was 23:8 (Figure 2). Caldwell pointed out that

> the interesting thing about the Wright propeller, however, is that the speed of rotation was chosen in such a way as to give the most favorable conditions for propeller efficiency, due to the fact that the ratio of rotational tip speed to forward speed of the airplane was incorrectly chosen.[7]

In 1904 four different propellers were used on the second airplane including the 1903 propellers. All the propellers were similar in shape to those of 1903. Blades of 7½, 8, 8¾ and 10 inch widths were used. Rotational speed was increased with a sprocket ratio 33:10. Consequently, thrust was increased. A notation of 185 pounds at 400 revolutions per minute for the 10-inch blade is mentioned in one notebook.

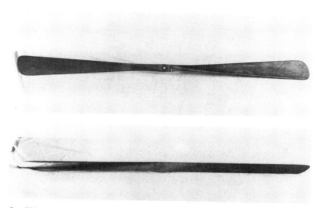

2. Wright 1903 propeller used on the first flight. (SI Neg. 42363C and 42363A)

The Wrights had found that propellers tended to twist under pressure and lose performance. In 1905 they redesigned their propellers. To reduce the twisting, a pie-shaped portion of the leading edge was removed resulting in a relatively constant blade width for 30 percent of the distance from the tip to the center. These propellers were called "bent end" type. From now on the Wrights continued the use of "bent ends" with variations. Most propellers were 8½ feet in diameter, though some were 9 feet in diameter. Blade widths ranged from 10 to 12 inches, pitch from 23 degrees to 27 degrees at the tips. Thrust on the 1905 "bent end" was 210 pounds at 450 revolutions per minute. Efficiency remained at 66 percent (Figure 3).

3. Wright 1905 "bent end" type propeller. (SI Neg. 18224A)

Construction of the "bent end" propellers was much the same as that of the 1903 type. The outer two-thirds of the blade was covered on both sides with light canvas which was glued on. The whole propeller was painted aluminum, lacquered, and polished.

With the thrust/propeller system determined, an energy source to drive the propellers was required. For this, the Wrights chose the internal combustion engine.

The 1903 Engine

The Wrights did not particularly want to get into the problem of designing and building an engine even though they previously had designed and built in 1901 their highly successful shop engine. This was a single-cylinder stationary power plant producing some three horsepower, air cooled, and operated on city illuminating gas.

With some hope that they could purchase a suitable engine, the Wrights sent a number of letters to various engine manufacturers inquiring for a gasoline engine developing eight to nine brake horsepower, weighing no more than 180 pounds, or an average of 20 pounds/horsepower and free from vibration. While at least ten replies were received, none met the desired specification.

In view of the state of the art at the time, no suitable engines were available. An established manufacturer would hesitate to undertake the development of such an engine that would have little market. Furthermore, the cost and time to produce such an engine would be more than the Wrights could afford. Apparently, the Wrights pursued this avenue no further and continued their plans to design and build their own engine.

To maintain cost control, the Wrights desired to machine engine parts as far as possible in their own shop. The metal-working machinery in the shop consisted only of a lathe, a drill press, and hand tools. Where complex machining operations were required, the Wrights had available in the Dayton area experienced machine shops with sophisticated equipment. Consequently, the meager equipment of the Wright shop added a design requirement to their engine. Work began upon the engine late December 1902.

The Wrights assigned to their mechanic, Charles E. Taylor, the job of actually machining and constructing the engine. He was more experienced in metal machining than they. Furthermore, their principal work was to be the construction of the first powered airframe. Little is known of the design process of the engine. According to Taylor, the Wrights included him in the many discussions and evaluations, but the decision making was theirs.[8]

Taylor said, "We didn't make any drawings. One of us would sketch out the part we were talking about on a piece of scratch paper and I'd spike the sketch over my bench.[9] No original drawings of the engine have ever been found. Furthermore, Orville Wright's diary of 1904 states, "Took old engine apart to get measurements for making new engine, an indication that drawings of the 1903 engine did not exist.[10] Consequently, it would appear that Taylor, applying to the sketches his knowledge of machining and experience of fitting, was essentially responsible for establishing the detail dimensioning of the engine. Undoubtedly, much of the detail design of the engine was his.

Studying the details of their engine, one is impressed in seeing the thought and consideration that went into the design. Obviously much forethought and careful design work preceded actual construction. There are no haphazard or "cobbled-up" solutions. All had been carefully laid out. For example, Taylor related:

> The first thing we did was to construct a sort of skeleton model, a test cylinder of about a four inch bore. The Wright boys were thorough that way. They wanted to see how some of the vital components worked before proceeding further. We hooked the test cylinder up to the shop power, smeared it with oil with a paint brush, and watched it run for short periods. It looked good; so we decided to go ahead with a four-cylinder model.[11]

This is all the more remarkable as the Wrights apparently made no detailed engineering drawings, only some temporary sketches. The intricate crankcase casting, for instance, shows evidence of much forethought on the overall engine design providing for webs, brackets, bosses, and contours to hold and support other engine parts. The records indicate that the Wrights made their own wood casting patterns.

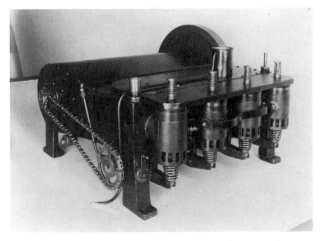

4. Wright 1903 engine chain-driven exhaust valve camshaft drive, valve boxes, and fuel line to air inlet can, spark advance/retard lever are visible. (SI Neg. 38626B)

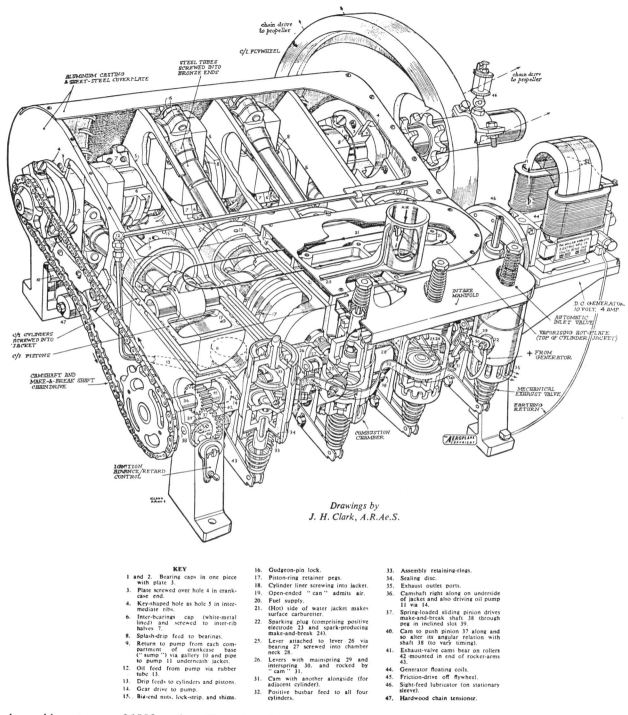

chain drive to propeller

c/I. FLYWHEEL

chain drive to propeller

ALUMINIUM CASTING & SHEET-STEEL COVERPLATE

STEEL TUBES SCREWED INTO BRONZE ENDS

46

45

44

D. C. GENERATOR. 10 VOLT. 4 AMP.

AUTOMATIC INLET VALVE

VAPORISING HOT-PLATE (TOP OF CYLINDER JACKET)

+ FROM GENERATOR

INTAKE MANIFOLD

AIR

c/I CYLINDERS SCREWED INTO JACKET

c/I PISTONS

CAMSHAFT AND MAKE-&-BREAK SHAFT CHAIN DRIVE

MECHANICAL EXHAUST VALVE

EARTHING RETURN

COMBUSTION CHAMBER

AEROPLANE COPYRIGHT

IGNITION ADVANCE/RETARD CONTROL

CLEAN AIR IN

Drawings by
J. H. Clark, A.R.Ae.S.

KEY

1 and 2. Bearing caps in one piece with plate 3.
3. Plate screwed over hole 4 in crank-case end.
4. Key-shaped hole as hole 5 in inter-mediate ribs.
6. Inter-bearings cap (white-metal lined) and screwed to inter-rib halves 7.
8. Splash-drip feed to bearings.
9. Return to pump from each com-partment of crankcase base ("sump") via gallery 10 and pipe to pump 11 underneath jacket.
12. Oil feed from pump via rubber tube 13.
13. Drip feeds to cylinders and pistons.
14. Gear drive to pump.
15. Big-end nuts, lock-strip, and shims.

16. Gudgeon-pin lock.
17. Piston-ring retainer pegs.
18. Cylinder liner screwing into jacket.
19. Open-ended "can" admits air.
20. Fuel supply.
21. (Hot) side of water jacket makes surface carburetter.
22. Sparking plug (comprising positive electrode 23 and spark-producing make-and-break 24).
25. Lever attached to lever 26 via bearing 27 screwed into chamber neck 28.
26. Levers with mainspring 29 and interspring 30. and rocked by " cam " 31.
31. Cam with another alongside (for adjacent cylinder).
32. Positive busbar feed to all four cylinders.

33. Assembly retaining-rings.
34. Sealing disc.
35. Exhaust outlet ports.
36. Camshaft right along on underside of jacket and also driving oil pump 11 via 14.
37. Spring-loaded sliding pinion drives make-and-break shaft 38 through peg in inclined slot 39.
40. Cam to push pinion 37 along and so alter its angular relation with shaft 38 (to vary timing).
41. Exhaust-valve cams bear on rollers 42 mounted in end of rocker-arms 43.
44. Generator floating coils.
45. Friction-drive off flywheel.
46. Sight-feed lubricator (on stationary sleeve).
47. Hardwood chain tensioner.

5. Assembly cutaway of 1903 engine. (From *Aeroplane*, photocopied UTC Archive A-113)

Probably these patterns served as three-dimensional drawings upon which design details could be worked out.

In laying out the engine design, the Wrights wished to produce an engine that would provide the perform-ance necessary to fly their airplane. They were not interested in producing an engine of the highest technical refinement, as such would be both costly and time-consuming. Their first decision was to select the size, number, and arrangement of the cylinders. The decision was much influenced by a primary concern of engine roughness. Vibration from the engine would deleteriously affect the structural integ-rity of both a lightweight engine and a frail airframe.

Their choice of four cylinders in-line was a practical choice, an arrangement serving well in the automotive field, and one that would provide reasonable smoothness in operation without undue complexity. It appears that the Wrights considered vibration to come largely from explosion forces which would be mitigated with multiple cylinders. They apparently did not take into account, or chose to ignore, the inherent shaking force in the four in-line arrangement which was about 91 pounds per cylinder (See Appendix 1). They chose a "square" four-by-four-inch size cylinder for reasons not recorded. However, this size provided a cylinder large enough not to penalize weight and small enough to ensure successful operation. This size, or slightly larger, was to remain standard on all subsequent Wright engines. The engine's displacement was 201 cubic inches (Figures 4 and 5).

"The Mean Effective Pressure (MEP) in the cylinder, based on their indicated goal of 8 hp, would be a very modest 36 psi at the speed of 870 rpm at which they first tested the engine, and only 31 psi at the reasonably conservative speed of 1000 rpm."[12] "Assuming a rich mixture, consumption of all the air, and an airbrake thermal efficiency of 24.50% for the original engine, the approximate volumetric efficiency of the cylinder is calculated to have been just under 40%."[13] (See Appendix 2).

The matter of cooling was also an important decision at this time. Their shop engine was air cooled. Air cooling had many weight-saving considerations. Yet, the Wrights opted for water cooling. At that time water-cooled engines were predominant in automobiles and were providing the best performance in general service. All subsequent Wright engines were of the water-cooled type.

The decision to arrange the engine in a horizontal position rather than the usual vertical position probably was to reduce drag or to spread the engine weight over a larger mounting base, or both.

On the detail design of the engine one of the most important decisions the Wrights had to make was that of the crankcase design and its cylinder arrangement. The Wrights were radical in choosing en-block construction. Most engines of that period had individual cylinders mounted upon the crankcase. In spite of the more complex design that an en-block, one-piece crankcase entailed, it eliminated the making and joining of a number of smaller pieces, hence saving both time and money. While machining of the crankcase may have required sending it to an outside machine shop, Taylor states that he bored out the cylinder mounting bores on the shop lathe.[14] Most of the machine work was of a nature which allowed it to be accomplished at the Wright shop. For lightness, the crankcase was cast in aluminium alloy of 8 percent copper and 92 percent aluminum. At that time alu-

6. 1903 disassembled cylinder with barrel, valve box, valves in cages, and rocker arm. (SI Neg. 38626G)

minum castings were used in many automobile engine crankcases. The Wright crankcase was designed so as to carry the major portion of the engine within, adding both strength and lightness to the engine. The open upper portion of the crankcase was covered with a screwed-on sheet steel plate.

Cast iron was employed for the cylinder, which was machined as thin as practical to save weight (Figure 6). The barrel was partially closed at the head end, terminating in a threaded boss. Installed through the interior of the crankcase, the barrel was screwed into the cylinder mounting bore seating on the outer and inner flange against the crankcase, thus forming the water jacket. A cast cylindrical valve box lay across the cylinder barrel, which contained the inlet and exhaust valves in cages. The valve box was screwed onto the threaded cylinder head boss, firmly tightening the barrel outer flange against the crankcase. The boss bore and the valve box formed the combustion chamber. Interestingly, the two cylinder barrel thread sets and flanges had to be accurately cut and fitted so that the screwing of the barrel into the crankcase and the valve box occurred in such a way to form a tight three-way joint. The valve box was strictly air cooled, which, however, became red hot after a few minutes' run (Figure 7).

The inlet valve was an "automatic" or suction-operated valve, which eliminated one complete mechanical valve-operating mechanism. The exhaust valve was mechanically operated by cams and rocker arms. The camshaft was driven by the crankshaft through a bicycle chain. Cast iron was employed for the entire valve system, except for cold-rolled steel valve stems.

The power machinery—that is, crankshaft, connecting rods, and pistons—was all made in the Wright shop. From a solid slab of heat-treated, relatively high carbon steel, Taylor cut and turned on the lathe the

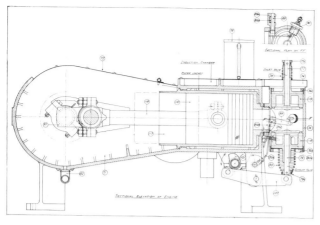

7. Cross section of 1903 engine showing cylinder and valve assembly in crankcase. (Science Museum, London, from UTC Archive A-112)

9. Underside of 1903 engine showing exhaust valve rocker arms, camshaft, spark advance/retard rod, and later added oil pump and lines. (SI Neg. 38626F)

four-throw crankshaft. The shaft was an orthodox straight pin and cheek type without counterweights. Large plain babbitted bearings on each side of the cranks provided added stiffness. The Wrights were fortunate that the vibratory forces were relatively small in their engines so that the natural vibration frequency always fell outside the small operating speed range of the engine. A machined 26 pound cast iron flywheel, balanced against the magnitude of the explosion force, was shrunk onto the crankshaft (Figure 8).

The connecting rods were made from seamless steel tubing and screwed and pinned into phosphor-bronze cast ends drilled through to form the bearings. For the first engine, this rod construction was satisfactory but proved to be troublesome in later engines. In the six-cylinder engine it was replaced by a rod of I section.

8. 1903 crankcase, open, showing power machinery. (SI Neg. 38626H)

The pistons were typical of the time, machined from cast iron with long skirts and accommodation for three cast iron piston rings.

The Wrights were very careful to control weight in the engine. Every part was weighed and recorded as it was finished so as to conform to their predetermined weight allowance.

As first built, the 1903 engine was splash lubricated internally and externally, with liberal applications from an oil can. When the engine was rebuilt in 1916, another or new crankcase was obtained to replace the original, which had been broken after the first flight and apparently melted down to make other castings. In the replacement crankcases an oil pump and pressure oil system was incorporated, which sprayed oil over the thrust-loaded side of each piston (Figure 9).

The fuel system was relatively simple. There was no carburetor as such. Fuel flowed by gravity from a 0.4 gallon gasoline tank mounted high on a strut through copper tubing to the engine. Two valves were placed in the fuel line; one was an on-off shut off valve, while the other was a regulating valve that could be adjusted to govern engine speed and power. Fuel was discharged into the top of a sheet metal "can," where it mixed with the incoming air and passed into an induction chamber. The mixture circulated over the hot surface of the crankcase, thereby vaporizing the mixture. The fuel/air mixture then passed into the intake manifold that surrounded the inlet valve and cage and on into the cylinders.

Two ignition systems, the high-tension spark plug and the low tension make-and-break, were in general use in 1902. The high-tension system was somewhat simpler but less reliable than the more complex make-and-break. Probably for reasons of reliability and the fact that all the parts could be made in the Wright shop or easily procured, the Wrights chose the low-tension make-and-break system. Also, this system was not susceptible to fouling from excess oil in the cylinders, an important consideration for a new engine design. The spark was made by the opening and closing of two contact points inside the combustion chamber. An insulated, fixed contact point in the combustion chamber was connected to the Miller-Knoblock 10 volt 4 amp D.C. magneto which was friction-driven by the flywheel. A movable contact point inside the combustion chamber was mounted on an arm whose shaft passed through the cylinder wall. The shaft was attached to a steel spring leaf that rode over a cam on the ignition camshaft. The camshaft was driven by the exhaust valve camshaft. Through a mechanism, control of the spark timing was accomplished by advancing or retarding the ignition camshaft in relation to the exhaust valve camshaft. Dry batteries and a coil were connected for starting but were not part of the airplane.

The cooling system consisted of a vertical radiator made from slightly flattened metal tubes connected to the engine water jacket with rubber "in" and "out" hoses. The cooling water circulated by convection.

The engine was completed in February 1903 and first run on February 12. The Wrights were pleased with its operation and smoothness. Then began a period of break-in and development. In the course of development, stronger valve springs were installed which increased power to nearly 16 horsepower and reduced fuel consumption by half. Orville wrote:

> Due to the preheating of the air by the water jacket and the red-hot valves and boxes, the air was greatly expanded before entering the cylinders. As a result, in a few minutes' time, the power dropped to less than 75 percent of what it was on cranking the motor. The highest speed ever measured was 300 turns (1,200 rpm) in the first fifteen seconds after starting the cold motor. The revolutions dropped rapidly and were down to 1,090 rpm after several minutes' run.[15]

According to the Wrights' measurements and calculations, the powers obtained at these speeds were 15.76 horsepower and 11.81 horsepower, respectively.[16]

For their first engine, the Wrights set out to produce one of 8 horsepower not to weigh more than 180 pounds. They calculated that this would be adequate to fly their machine. That they met this requirement is attested in a letter Wilbur wrote to George Spratt dated February 28, 1903:

> We recently built a four-cylinder gasoline engine with 4″ stroke, to see how powerful it would be, and what it would weigh. At 670 rpm it developed 8¼ horsepower, brake test. By speeding it up to 1,000 rpm we will easily get 11 horsepower and possibly a little more at still higher speed, though the increase is not in exact proportion to the increase in number

of revolutions. The weight including the 30-pound flywheel is 140 lbs.

Orville stated that the engine weighed 161 pounds dry and 179 pounds with the magneto.[17] "Complete with magneto, radiator, tank, water, fuel, tubing and accessories the powerplant weighed a little over 200 pounds."[18] The Wrights met their objective, and more.

With a suitable and satisfactory engine, the Wrights went on to achieve their first powered flight with it on December 17, 1903.[19]

> It is remarkable that these two men, aided by Taylor, inexperienced in internal combustion engine design and especially multi-cylinder engines—much less in extra light construction—could, in two months, bring through an engine which was both operable and somewhat lighter than their specification.[20]

The 1904 Engines

To continue flying and perfecting their mastery of flight, the Wrights in 1904 undertook to build a new airplane and engines to power it. Three more powerful engines were put into construction. Two engines were based upon the 1903 engine design, while the third was one of eight cylinders. Little is known about this eight-cylinder engine. As the four-cylinder engines were producing sufficiently more power, the eight-cylinder engine was not completed and the parts were scrapped.

The first 1904 four-cylinder engine was merely an improved 1903 and was designated No. 2. It had a bore of 4⅛ inches, an oil pump, a fuel pump, and a 10 percent increase of cylinder barrel water cooling. Its displacement was 214 cubic inches. Its one unusual new feature was the addition of a compression release mechanism. The pilot actuated a sliding shaft that forced stops under the exhaust valve rocker arm rollers and kept the valves open thus effectively shutting off the engine. Why the Wrights incorporated a compression release has never been fully explained. It was, however, useful in starting and stopping. It was continued on all subsequent engines (Figure 10).

Initially, the No. 2 engine developed 15 to 16 horsepower. By 1905 it was developing 20 to 21 horsepower. Most of the subsequent gain was due to the smoothing of the cylinders and pistons by wear.[21] This engine was employed in the 1904 airplane and also in the 1905 airplane.[22]

Engine No. 3 was built in 1904 for experimental purposes. The two objectives, in providing this engine, were to improve performance and reliability. The engine was operated extensively on a test stand from 1904 until mid-1906. It had a four-inch bore and incorporated compression release and exhaust ports in the cylinder barrels. Several holes were drilled in

10. A 1904 No. 3 experimental engine with compression release mechanism. (UTC Archive A-108)

the barrel which were uncovered by the piston at the end of its stroke. The purpose of the exhaust ports was to reduce the pressure and temperature of the exhaust gas passing through the exhaust valve. Exhaust ports were also used on the subsequent four-cylinder vertical engines. By 1906, No. 3 engine was developing 24 to 25 horsepower at 1300 revolutions per minute, twice the power of the original 1903 engine of the same size.[23]

The Four-Cylinder Vertical Engine

In 1906, while still doing general development work on the flat experimental engine, the Wrights started two new engines, and for the first time the brothers engaged in separate efforts. One was "a modification of the old ones" by Wilbur and the other, "an entirely new pattern" by Orville. There is no record of any of the features of Wilbur's project or what was done in connection with it.

There is a brief entry on it in Wilbur's diary but no further mention of it.[24] Orville's design was a four-cylinder vertical engine which was to become the most used of any model they produced. Production of this engine continued into 1912. From now on there are indications that Orville became the leader in engine design.

Orville's engine represented significant change from the previous horizontal type. Hobbs concluded that "putting the engine in an upright instead of flat position, was probably done primarily to provide for a minimum variation in the location of the center of gravity with and without a passenger."[25]

Initially the four-cylinder vertical engines delivered 28 horsepower at 1325 revolutions per minute and weighed 160 pounds dry. Throughout its production run many changes and improvements were made so that its power ultimately reached 40 horsepower at 1500 revolutions per minute at a dry weight of 180 pounds. These engines had a bore of 4⅜ inches, a stroke of 4 inches, and a displacement of 240 inches. The engines generally were reliable though trouble was often experienced with exhaust valves, pistons, and cylinders (Figure 11).

The most drastic change from the previous engines was the employment of individual cylinders and the abandonment of en-block construction (Figure 12). Again the sturdy aluminum alloy crankcase was cast in one piece with one side open and covered with a screwed-on sheet-steel plate. The cylinders were bolted to the flat top of the crankcase. However, many of the details were similar to those of the original

11. Four-cylinder vertical engine (1906–12), right side showing fuel system injection pump and line to fuel-air manifold, and oil system pressure lines from sump to pump to crankcase and oil fill pipe. (SI Neg. 36895D)

12. Left side view of four-cylinder vertical engine with crankcase open to expose the power machinery. Compression release rod is mounted along top of crankcase. Mea magneto installed. Water circulation pump at far left. (P&W photo, UTC Archive D-15006)

13. **Four-throw crankshaft cut from steel blank and shrunk-on flywheel.** (P&W photo, UTC Archive D-14999)

14. **Tubular connecting rod screwed into cast ends. Pointed oil scupper is mounted on crankshaft bearing cap.** (P&W photo, UTC Archive D-14992)

engine, even though involving some modifications and improvements. Such parts were the crankshaft and flywheel (Figure 13), pistons, two-piece inlet and exhaust valves, rocker arms, and connecting rods (Figure 14). See Appendix IV for material composition and hardness of these parts.

The cylinder was a complete one-piece iron casting, machined all over. Inlet and exhaust ports and valve guides were cut into an integral boss on the head of the cylinder. The inlet valve again was an "automatic" type, while the exhaust valve was mechanically operated. The exhaust rocker arm rocked on a steel stud screwed into the cylinder head and was actuated by a pushrod operated by the cam shaft inside the crankcase. A four-cornered flange near the bottom of the cylinder provided for fastening the cylinder to the crankcase. A cast aluminum water jacket was shrunk onto the cylinder barrels and covered about two-thirds of the barrel. The lower part of the barrel was not cooled because of the exhaust ports drilled into the barrel wall. Also, the cylinder had remained uncooled (Figures 15 and 16).

A pressurized lubrication system was incorporated. An oil pump driven by the camshaft pumped oil from the sump and forced it through drilled passages in the crankshaft and crankcase to lubricate the bearings, cams, and cylinders. A scupper on the crankshaft end of the connecting rod threw oil onto the cylinders.

Gravity-fed gasoline from a tank mounted high in the struts went to a camshaft-driven fuel pump that metered the fuel, as there was no carburetor. The fuel entered a baffled inlet manifold where it mixed with air and was heated by the exhaust impinging on the manifold before entering the cylinder.

A water circulation pump driven by the crankshaft was incorporated. Cooling water was piped to a horizontal manifold at the top of the cylinders and after circulation around the cylinders was collected in another horizontal manifold on the other side of the cylinders for return to the radiator. A normally supplied vertical tube radiator weighed 40 pounds and carried 25 pounds of water.

Now the Wrights installed a high tension ignition system. A Mea magneto, though sometimes a Bosch, was mounted on a bracket, cast integral on the crankcase and driven through gears from the camshaft. One spark plug was installed in each cylinder. By a foot pedal, the pilot controlled the spark advance which was the only speed control for the engine.

A revised compression release mechanism was installed. It lifted a collar on the pushrods to open the exhaust valve and stop the engine.

The four-cylinder vertical engine was the only engine licensed by the Wrights for manufacture by

15. **Cylinder assembly, push rod, rocker arm, and camshaft.** (P&W photo, UTC Archive D-14996)

16. **Disassembled cylinder showing cast iron barrel, cast aluminum water jacket, and two-piece valves.** (P&W photo, UTC Archive D-15001)

Harvey H. Lippincott

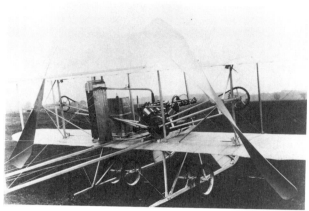

17. Propulsion system of 1910 Baby Grand Racer with eight-cylinder engine installed. (SI Neg. # A-42408)

18. Early six-cylinder engine (1911) with fuel/air mixing manifold and exhaust ports adjacent to inlet parts. (U.S. Air Force Museum, photocopied from UTC Archive A-111)

others. In Germany these engines were manufactured by Neue Automobil-Gesellschaft and in France by Bariquand et Marré. While no production figures exist, recollections of a factory foreman indicates a hundred engines were manufactured, if not more.

The Eight-Cylinder Racing Engine

The Wrights decided to enter an airplane in the 1910 Gordon Bennett Cup Race. A small racing airplane was built. The 30 horsepower four-cylinder vertical engine was considered to be too small. They designed and built a 60 horsepower Vee-eight of 481 cubic inch displacement. It was essentially a combination of two standard four-cylinder engines on a special crankcase spread 90 degrees apart. The connecting rods were placed side-by-side on a modified four-cylinder crankshaft. A single camshaft operated all the exhaust valves. The engine weighed about 300 pounds (Figure 17).

Unfortunately, the engine had a short life as the airplane was demolished before the race. Little information on it survives.

The Six-Cylinder Vertical Engines

By 1911, as aircraft performance improved, the Wrights faced the necessity of equipping their airplanes with more powerful engines in the race to keep up with their competition. They had three choices: (1) increase the size of their four-cylinder engine; (2) develop their eight-cylinder engine; or (3) produce a six-cylinder engine. Dimensional increase in bore and stroke of the four-cylinder engine would increase operational roughness which the Wrights did not want. An eight-cylinder engine would probably be too large for their needs at that time. Their choice of a six-cylinder arrangement gave them the desired power

19. 6–60 six-cylinder engine (1912–13) exhaust side. (SI Neg. 74828)

with a very smooth operation. Also, it continued their experience with in-line engines.

The cylinder bore remained at 4⅜ inches. However, the stroke was lengthened ½ inch to 4½ inches in order to increase displacement, which was 406 cubic inches. Early six-cylinder engines produced 50 horsepower (Figure 18). In 1913 the engine was redesigned. Called the 6-60, it gave 60 horsepower (Figure 19). The final version, the 6-70, produced 75 horsepower. One may ask why the Wrights did not produce more powerful engines, as did their competition who were turning out 80-100 horsepower engines. The answer probably lies in the high efficiency of their propellers, which required less power to produce the same thrust.

While many of the four-cylinder engine parts were utilized in the six-cylinder engine, there were several significant differences and improvements. The cast aluminum crankcase was two pieces split along the horizontal crankshaft centerline. The upper crankcase was open on one side covered with a screwed-on sheet-steel plate. The crankshaft was supported in the upper crankcase only. The lower crankcase supported the engine and provided for its mounting (Figure 20).

20. Six-cylinder two-piece crankcase. (P&W photo, UTC Archive D-15015)

A major improvement was in the cylinders. The three-piece cylinder consisted of a machined, cast iron barrel with a section of seamless steel tube shrunk on to form a water jacket, while a cast iron head was shrunk on to the top of the barrel. For the first time the head was water cooled. Four long studs running from the crankcase to the top of the cylinder head held the cylinders in place. Also, for the first time, one-piece forged steel valves were used, though strangely only for the inlet. The more critical exhaust valve was still the old two-piece type with a cast iron head and steel stem. Exhaust ports in the lower part

21. Cylinder and valves for early six-cylinder engine. (P&W photo, UTC Archive D-15014)

of the barrel were no longer used. On the early sixes, automatic inlet valves were employed. These were replaced with mechanically operated valves in the 6-60. The exhaust valves had the same compression release mechanism as the vertical four (Figure 21).

The power machinery followed similar lines of the vertical four. The pistons were shortened an inch, saving 40 percent of their weight. For the first time forgings were used in the crankshaft and I-section connecting rods (Figures 22 and 23).

22. Six-cylinder forged crankshaft and flywheel. (P&W photo, UTC Archive D-15018)

23. Six-cylinder forged I section connecting rod and piston. (P&W photo, UTC Archive D-15017)

Early engines continued use of the fuel injection pump and manifold. Vaporization problems apparently were encountered in the longer manifold which now was unheated. The old system was replaced in the 6-60 with two float-feed Zenith carburetors, each feeding three cylinders (Figure 24).

For the 6-60 the cylinders were redesigned so that inlet and exhaust ports were on opposite sides of the cylinder, rather than side-by-side as on the earlier sixes. This arrangement facilitated the installation of mufflers.

The six-cylinder engine was a vastly improved engine, especially in its final form. Aesthetically, it

24. 6–60 six-cylinder engine with twin Zenith carburetors. (SI Neg. 74829)

was an attractive engine showing spare design, simplicity, and utility.

Concluding Remarks

Summing up, Hobbs said:

> Overall, the Wright engines performed well, and in every case met or exceeded the existing requirements. Even though aircraft engines then were simpler than they became later and the design-development time much shorter, their performance stands as remarkable. As a result, the Wrights never lacked for a suitable powerplant despite the rapid growth in airplane size and performance, and the continual demand for increased power and endurance.[26]

As with all machines, there were problems and failures. Lubrication was a continuing problem, especially in the early years. Piston and cylinder barrel bearing surfaces had much distress with frequent scuffing and seizures, apparently due largely to poor lubrication and tight clearances. Broken and cracked cylinders were frequent. Valve failures were a constant annoyance. Part of the valve problem was caused by the cam design, which created rapid valve opening accelerations and high valve seating velocities. The Wright engine problems were no worse, and perhaps not as severe, as those of their competition.

Nevertheless, the Wright brothers showed remarkable engineering talent in the field of propulsion. With no prior experience, they carefully analyzed the problem, as they had with their airplane, and devised good, basic engines of simple, sound design. Hobbs, one of the great aero engine engineers of all time, evaluated the Wrights' engineering.

> For the engineer particularly, the fascination of the Wrights' engine story lies in its delineation of the essentially perfect engineering achievement by the classic definition of engineering—to utilize the available art and science to accomplish the desired end with a minimum expenditure of time, energy and material.[27]

Harvey H. Lippincott, a native of Moorestown, New Jersey, holds a B.S. in Mechanical Engineering from Georgia Institute of Technology. He held various positions in product support and marketing of aircraft engines with Pratt and Whitney Aircraft from 1941 to 1972 when he became Corporate Archivist for United Technologies. In 1959 he founded the Connecticut Aeronautical Historical Association and served as president of that organization for eight years. He has collaborated with many aviation museums and in 1961 founded the Bradley Air Museum and served as its director. He is Chairman and member representing eastern United States of the Steering Committee for the Aviation Museum Directors and Curators Committee For the International Association of Transport Museums. He serves on the State Historical Records Advisory Board and the Northeast Document Conservation Center Advisory Committee. He is a member of New England Archivists and Association for Study of Connecticut History.

Notes

1. Frank W. Caldwell, "Notes on the History of Aircraft Propellers," circulated unpublished tract, Hamilton Standard Series, United Technologies Archives, May 1, 1939, p. 1. Caldwell was Chief of the Propeller Engineering Division, Army Air Service, 1916–28; Chief Engineer, Standard Steel Propeller Company (later Hamilton Standard Propeller Company) 1929–35; Engineering Manager, Hamilton Standard Propeller Division, United Aircraft Corporation 1935–40; Director of Research, United Aircraft Corporation 1940–54; and winner of the Collier Trophy for 1933 for development of the controllable pitch propeller.

2. Orville and Wilbur Wright, "The Wright Brothers' Aeroplane," *The Century Magazine*, September 1908, Vol. 76, pp. 641–50.

3. Orville Wright, "How We Made the Flight," *Flying*, December 1913, Vol. 2, pp. 10–12, 35–36.

4. Ibid.

5. Marvin W. McFarland, ed., *The Papers of Wilbur and Orville Wright*, McGraw-Hill Book Co., New York, 1935. Note bottom p. 617.

6. Leonard S. Hobbs, "The Wright Brothers' Engines and Their Design," *Smithsonian Annals of Flight, Number 5,* Smithsonian Institution Press, Washington, D.C. 1971, p. 12. Hobbs joined Pratt & Whitney Aircraft in 1927 as Research Engineer, advanced in the Engineering Department to become the Engineering Manager in 1935, and became Vice President for Engineering at United Aircraft Corporation 1944–56.

7. Caldwell, p. 1.

8. Fred F. Marshall, "Building the Original Wright Brothers Engine," *Slipstream Aviation Monthly,* May 1928, Dayton, Ohio. An article based upon a personal interview by the author with Charles E. Taylor.

9. Charles E. Taylor as told to Robert S. Ball, "My Story of the Wright Brothers," *Collier's,* December 26, 1948, Vol. 122 (26), p. 27.

10. McFarland, p. 414; Orville Wright's Diary, Thursday, January 14, 1904.

11. Marshall.

12. Hobbs, p. 10.

13. Hobbs, p. 20.

14. Taylor, p. 68.

15. McFarland, p. 1210–13.

16. Ibid.

17. Orville Wright to Charles L. Lawrence, November 15, 1928.

18. McFarland, p. 1212.

19. The restored 1903 engine is installed in the restored 1903 airplane on display at the National Air and Space Museum, Smithsonian Institution, Washington, D.C. The engine was restored in 1916. In 1906 the crankshaft and flywheel were loaned to the Aero Club of America for their first aero show in New York. They were never returned. Therefore, the 1904 crankshaft and flywheel were installed in a new crankcase, which incorporated an oil pump and pressure oil system.

20. Hobbs, p. 27.

21. Orville Wright letter to Charles L. Lawrence, November 15, 1928.

22. The 1904 No. 2 engine was restored in 1948 without a crankshaft and installed in the restored 1905 airplane on display at Wright Hall, Carillon Park, Dayton, Ohio.

23. The No. 3 engine is on display at the Engineers Club in Dayton, Ohio.

24. Hobbs, p. 34.

25. Hobbs, p. 34.

26. Hobbs, p. 59.

27. Hobbs, p. 61.

Appendix 1

Balance of Wright 1903 Engine

In 1966 L. Morgan Porter, Analytical Engineer, Pratt & Whitney Aircraft, analyzed the balance of the Wright 1903 engine for Leonard Hobbs's study of the Wright brothers' engines and reported:

> This four cylinder in-line engine of 4 inch bore and 4 inch stroke had a five main bearing flat crankshaft with cranks 1 and 4 at 180 degrees from 2 and 3. With this type crankshaft the primary inertia forces and resulting rocking couples are inherently balanced among themselves. However, since this engine had no crankshaft counterweights, the primary inertia forces, in addition to the gas forces, are felt by the main bearings. At 1200 rpm this inertia force amounts to about 455 pounds in line with each cylinder, but with the direction at cylinders 1 and 4 opposite to that at cylinders 2 and 3.
>
> For the second and all higher harmonics, there being no odd orders above the first, the inertia forces for all cylinders are in the same direction, and while this results in no rocking couples, there is a shaking force in line with the cylinders, the magnitude of which is four times that for one cylinder. At 1200 rpm this secondary unbalanced shaking force amounts to about 91 pounds per cylinder, or a total force of 364 pounds. With the engine mounted horizontally in the airplane this resulted in a lateral shaking force on the engine supports occurring at twice crankshaft speed. Higher harmonics are usually neglected since their magnitudes become progressively smaller. The magnitudes of the primary

and secondary inertia forces were determined in the following manner.

Since actual reciprocating weights of the 1903 engine were unavailable, an estimate was made from the following data for the 1908 engine[2] in which the bore had been increased to 4.375 inches. Piston and Rings, 4 lb. 7 oz.; Piston Pin, 8 oz.; Connecting Rod, Cap, Bolts and Nuts, 2 lb. 3 oz. of which 1 lb. was assumed to be reciprocating weight.

Then for the 1903 engine, correcting the weight of the piston and rings directly as the cylinder bore, and taking the other weights the same (this neglects the increased connecting rod length of the 1903 engine, 10 inches compared to 9.25 inches for the 1908 engine), we have

Piston and Rings $(4.000/4.375)(4.4375) = 4.06$ lb.
Piston Pin plus Conn Rod Reciprocating $\underline{1.50}$
Total Inertia Weight $= 5.56$ lb.

The primary inertia force is given by

$$F_i = 28.4\, W_i\, R \left(\frac{N}{100}\right)^2 \cos \Theta$$

Where W_i = Reciprocating Weight, lb.
R = Crank Radius, in
N = rpm
Θ = Crank Angle From Top Dead Center

The max. value is then

$$F_i = 28.4\,(5.56)(2)(1.2)^2 = 454.5 \text{ lb}$$

The secondary inertia force is given by

$$F_i = 28.4\, W_i\, R \left(\frac{N}{1000}\right)^2 \left(\frac{R}{L}\right) \cos 2\Theta$$

Where L = Conn Rod Length, in

The max. value is then

$$F_i = 28.4\,(5.56)(2)(1.2)^2 \left(\frac{2}{10}\right) = 90.7 \text{ lb}$$

Notes

1. Internal memorandum L. M. Porter to G. N. Cole, Chief Design Engineer, Pratt & Whitney, dated May 26, 1966; Leonard S. Hobbs papers, Series 1, Smithsonian Monograph, Folder 22, United Technologies Archives.

2. Porter had available a 4-cylinder vertical engine of 1911 upon which an engineering analysis had been conducted.

Appendix 2

Volumetric Efficiency of Wright 1903 Engine

In 1966 L. Morgan Porter, Analytical Engineer of Pratt & Whitney Aircraft, conducted a study of the volumetric efficiency of the 1903 engine by extrapolating data from tests conducted on a single cylinder

Harvey H. Lippincott

engine with a Pratt & Whitney R-2800 cylinder. Based upon Porter's study,[1] the volumetric efficiency ranged from about 37% to 42% and was derived as follows:

Volumetric efficiency is defined as the ratio of the weight of air actually taken into the cylinder to the weight of air that would exactly fill the piston displacement at the inlet density. It is thus a figure of merit that can be used to compare the pumping ability of engines of different sizes or speeds. Volumetric efficiency is dimensionless, and may be greater or less than unity.[2]

$$e_v = \frac{2M_i}{NV_d\rho_i}$$

where M_1 = mass of fresh mixture per unit time
N = number of revolutions per unit time
V_d = total displacement volume of the engine
ρ = inlet density

The denominator of this expression can readily be determined once the engine speed, displacement, and inlet air density are determined. For unsupercharged engines the inlet density may be taken at standard conditions of 60°F and a pressure of 14.7 psi if the volumetric efficiency is to be based on conditions at the entrance to the carburetor. This will give the volumetric efficiency as a measure of the pumping ability of the entire engine.

As for the numerator of the expression for volumetric efficiency, the only accurate way to determine this is to actually measure the weight of air consumed by the engine in a given time with all other conditions, such as fuel-air ratio, speed, power, etc., remaining constant. For the Wright engine with its ported cylinders the actual air measurement would be a problem. Furthermore, the power did not remain constant, falling from 16 to 12 hp after warm-up. Therefore, any value of volumetric efficiency for this engine based on brake horsepower and speed must be considered an approximation only.

Porter arrived at a method that should give a fair indication of the volumetric efficiency of the 1903 engine based on an assumed value for the brake thermal efficiency.

Employing the equation:

$$P = JM_a (FQ_c) \eta$$

where P = power developed
J = mechanical equivalent of heat
M_a = mass flow of dry air per unit time, or air capacity
Q_c = heat of combustion per unit mass of fuel
η = thermal efficiency, which may be indicated or brake, depending upon whether P is defined as indicated or brake power

F = fuel-air ratio

and transposing the equation:

$$M_a = \frac{P}{J(FQ_c)\eta}$$

If the value of P is taken as 15.76 BHP as calculated by Orville Wright to be the maximum power obtained,[3] and Ricardo's FQ_c value of 1290 BTU per pound as the heating value of air when burned with gasoline (based on a stochiometric mixture with fuel of about 19,000 BTU per pound).

$\frac{p}{FQ_c}$ will give the weight of air consumed equivalent

to the BHP output. Then dividing this by J of 778 ft-lbs per BTU and by the brake thermal efficiency η, an indication of the total air consumption of the engine is obtained.

This method, of course, should only be used where the correct or rich mixtures are used, and depending on the accuracy of the air brake thermal efficiency (a function of the brake specific air consumption), will give the correct value for the air consumption for the BHP developed based on the assumption that all the air combines with the fuel. The air brake thermal efficiency (thermal efficiency based on air consumption) is used since any excess fuel is wasted and efficiency values based on the fuel consumption would be too low.

With an assumed air brake thermal efficiency of about 24.5%, explained later, the total air consumption is:

$$M_a = \frac{(15.76 \text{ BHP}) (33,000 \text{ ft. lbs/min/HP})}{(778 \text{ ft-lbs/BTU})(1290 \text{ BTU/lbs air}) (.245)}$$

$$M_a = 2.115 \frac{\text{lb. air}}{\text{min.}}$$

The volumetric efficiency for a four-stroke cycle engine, such as the 1903 engine, is expressed by the formula:

$$e_v = \frac{2M_i}{NV_d\rho_i}$$

where M_i = mass of fresh mixture per unit time
N = number of revolutions per unit time
V_d = total displacement volume of the engine
ρ_i = inlet density
2 = two crank revolutions per cycle

in which the mass of fresh mixture which passes into the cylinder in one suction stroke is divided by the mass of this mixture which would fill the piston displacement at inlet density.

The engine displacement (4 inch bore, 4 inch stroke, 4 cylinders) is 201 cubic inches. Engine speed at maximum power is 1200 rpm; then the swept volume of the engine is:

$$\frac{V_d N}{2} = \frac{201\ \text{in}^3}{1728\ \text{in}^3/\text{ft}^3} \times \frac{1200\ \text{rev/min}}{2\ \text{rev}} = \frac{69.792\ \text{ft}^3}{\text{min}}$$

Standard air density at the inlet is:

$$\rho = 0.0764\ \text{lb. air/ft}^3$$

and when multiplied by the swept volume is

$$\left(\frac{69.792\ \text{ft}^3}{\text{min}}\right)\left(\frac{.0764\ \text{lbs. air}}{\text{ft}^3}\right) = \frac{5.332\ \text{lbs air}}{\text{min}}$$

Then Volumetric Efficiency = 2.115/5.332
= 0.397 or 39.7%

Determination of the assumed air brake thermal efficiency (η) was based upon data from experimental tests conducted on a single cylinder engine using a Pratt & Whitney R-2800 cylinder.

To use the air brake thermal efficiency of the R-2800 single cylinder engine to estimate the air brake thermal efficiency for the 1903 engine, it would appear that this should be done at the 1200 rpm speed of the 1903 engine. However, 1600 rpm was the lowest speed at which the R-2800 single cylinder would operate satisfactorily at atmospheric conditions and a fuel-air ratio of .075.

The assumed thermal efficiency of 24.5% for the 1903 engine was arrived at by correcting the thermal efficiency of 28.95% at 1600 rpm for the R-2800 single

cylinder, thought to be about optimum for atmospheric conditions, directly as the ratio of the air cycle efficiency at an assumed expansion ratio of 4.5 for the 1903 engine to that for an expansion ratio of 6.75 for the R-2800. This gives (.452/.534)(.2895) = .2450 or 24.5% brake thermal efficiency.

Again assuming an expansion ratio of 4.00 for the 1903 engine instead of 4.50 as used above, similar calculations lead to a brake thermal efficiency of 23.09% and a volumetric efficiency of 42.1%. For an expansion ratio of 5.00 the results are 25.7% and 37.7%, respectively.

This analysis puts the volumetric efficiency of the 1903 engine in the range of about 37% to 42%. The validity of these results depends, of course, on the assumption of a rich mixture, that all the air is consumed, and the accuracy of the assumed thermal efficiency. However, the results are believed to be the best available with the data at hand.

Notes

1. Internal memoranda L. M. Porter to L. S. Hobbs and G. N. Cole, Pratt & Whitney Aircraft, dated July 15, 1966, and August 19, 1966, Leonard S. Hobbs papers, Series 1, Smithsonian Monograph, Folder 22, United Technologies Archives.

2. C. F. Taylor and E. S. Taylor, "The Internal Combustion Engine," International Textbook Co., Scranton, Penn. 1949.

3. Marvin W. McFarland, ed., *The Papers of Wilbur and Orville Wright*, McGraw-Hill Book Co., New York, 1953, pp. 1210–13.

APPENDIX 3

In 1966 Pratt & Whitney Aircraft disassembled and analyzed a Wright brothers 1911 four-cylinder vertical engine belonging to the National Air and Space Museum, Catalog No. M-1952-108. Material composition and hardness tests were conducted on several major steel components. Results of these tests are given in the following table and are characteristic of Wright engines:

Material and Hardness—Wright Brothers Engine 1908–1910

Part Name	Material—Approximate Composition	Hardness as taken R-15N	R-15T	Equivalent Hardness R-C	Bhn	Remarks
Crankshaft	1.5Cr 2.Ni .3Si .2 Mn Alloy Steel	71–72		24	248	
Camshaft	Carbon Steel	51	81–82			Shaft Portion
		51	84			Unworn Cam Area
		67		15.5	207	Worked Cam Area
Piston Pin	1.5 Cr 3.Ni .3 Si .2 Mn Alloy Steel	66	90		183	
Push Rod	Carbon Steel	63	89.5		176	
Rocker Roller		71		23	241	
Main Bearing	6–8 Cu 6–8 Sb. .2Pb Bal. Sn					Solid Babitt Shell

Structural Design of the 1903 Wright Flyer

HOWARD S. WOLKO

Introduction

When Wilbur and Orville Wright turned from making bicycles to making airplanes virtually only the powered flying machine remained an unsolved—and some said insoluble—problem. But the Wrights were convinced rational design was the key to proper construction of a flying machine. What sets their work apart from that of other would-be flying machine builders is their reliance on gliding experience and proven theory for design guidance.

The Wright brothers' understanding of aerodynamics, stability, control, and propulsion is discussed at some length in other papers in this publication. This work is limited to their appreciation of the interplay among these topics during design and the way in which theory influenced the Flyer's structural form.

From a design perspective, the structural form of the Flyer is not incidental. It is a consequence of the Wright brothers' understanding of the principles of air flow at the time of construction, of their choice, sizing, and disposition of materials in order to produce a machine strong enough yet light enough to fly with an engine of reasonable power, and of their great concern for safety. When all of these factors are taken into account we begin to appreciate how well the Wright brothers understood the art of aircraft design.

Configuration

By the latter part of the nineteenth century, structural analysis had emerged as one of the most advanced of the engineering arts. Methods of analysis common to all structural work were conveniently summarized in engineering handbooks such as Trautwein's *Civil Engineers' Pocketbook* of 1888 and Kents' *Mechanical Engineers' Handbook* of 1896. However, it remained to apply these general methods to design of a flight structure, and this requires a configuration and a means of estimating loads.

The Wrights' preference for a biplane arrangement can be traced to Wilbur's concept for achieving lateral control by warping the lifting surface of a "double-deck" machine similar to that tested by Chanute and Herring in 1869–97 (Reference 1). When their biplane kite experiment of 1899 showed the concept could be made to work without loss of structural stiffness, the Wrights chose to use a biplane configuration for their manned gliders. Wilbur later elaborated on the choice in an address presented before the Western Society of Engineers in 1901. While discussing the problem of control, he cited the prior work of Chanute and stated, "The double-deck machine built and tried at the same time (by Chanute) marked a very great structural advance as it was the first in which the principles of the modern truss bridges were fully applied to flying machine construction" (Reference 2).

However, as used by Chanute the fully trussed biplane structure was incompatible with the Wrights' scheme for obtaining lateral control by warping the wings to present the right and left sides at different angles of attack. The Wrights' ability to modify the system of trussing to accommodate wing warp without compromising the structural integrity of the biplane cellule is a convincing example of their design inge-

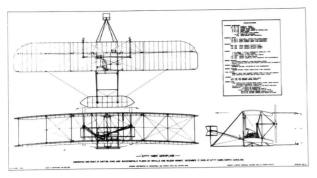

1. Three-view drawing of the Flyer

nuity and familiarity with structural behavior.

As finally evolved on the 1903 Flyer, shown in Figure 1, the central bays of the biplane cellule are completely trussed on all four sides to form a rigid, warp-free box, while the outer bays are rigidly trussed in the plane of the front spars only. Control wires, which also function as flying and landing wires, are used to truss the outer bays in the plane of the rear spars. With this arrangement the wing structure forms a complete load-carrying system for resisting the vertical loads and bending moments encountered in flight (Reference 3).

The Wrights' method for resisting lateral and longitudinal forces on the wing deserves particular attention since their 1903 machine did not have a drag truss in the plane of the lifting surfaces. Instead, it used the fabric covering as a shear web. By orienting the warp and woof of the fabric at 45 degrees to the spars, the rectangular wing structure is made sufficiently stable to withstand lateral and longitudinal forces while retaining its ability to twist (Reference 4).

To enable the aft part of the wings to be warped to either an up or down position, the wing ribs were made in two parts with the plane of separation at the rear spar. The ribs were then rejoined with two thin flat strips of spring steel attached to the rib caps above and below the rear spar. These spring steel "hinges" improved reliability while reducing the amount of force required to warp the wings.

A final touch of design detail is found in the hinged connectors that join the struts to the wing spars. By use of hinged connectors that function like universal joints the wing could be warped without imposing eccentric loads on the structural members.

When all of these modifications to the Chanute trussed biplane structure are taken into account, one begins to better appreciate how closely Wilbur and Orville Wright paid attention to design detail.

Undoubtedly the most distinctive (and controversial) feature of the Flyer is its forward mounted elevator. But the Wrights' choice of a canard config-

uration is clearly explained in Orville Wrights' letter to Alexander Klemin on April 24, 1924 (Reference 5). In Orville's words: "We originally put the elevators in front at a negative angle to provide a system of inherent stability. . . . We found it produced inherent instability. We then tried using our 1900 glider backwards with the rear edges foremost and found the stability much improved; but we retained the elevator in front for many years because it absolutely prevented a nose dive such as that in which Lilienthal and many others since have met their deaths." Thus, the Wrights' choice of a canard configuration is seen to have resulted from their concern for stall recovery and was a conscious decision in which safety played a dominant role. To them, control—not stability— was the main problem requiring attention.

Preliminary Design

Historians have always felt somewhat uncertain of how the Wrights went about designing their flying machines. A careful reading of *The Papers of Wilbur and Orville Wright*, edited by Marvin McFarland, reveals they started with a clearly defined objective and with this objective in mind prepared appropriate design specifications. Thus, Wilbur and Orville Wright functioned in much the same way as any project engineer today.

On December 11, 1902 (Reference 6) Wilbur disclosed their objective to Octave Chanute in a letter in which he writes: "It is our intention next year to build a machine much larger and about twice as heavy as our present machine (the 1902 glider). With it we will work out problems relating to starting and handling heavy weight machines, and if we find it under satisfactory control in flight, we will proceed to mount a motor." Apparently this objective was later modified for there is no record of any attempt to fly the 1903 machine as a glider. However, Wilbur's statement suggests their plan was defined in order to enable them to obtain maximum benefit from their previous design experience with gliders.

Their design specifications, shown in Figure 2, were extracted from Orville's letters to George Spratt on June 7, 1903 (Reference 7), and Charles Taylor, their mechanic, on November 23 (Reference 8) of the same year. These specifications indicate their original plan was to build a machine with a wing area of 500 square feet. From their experience with gliders, it was estimated that a machine of this size would weigh 625 pounds when fitted with a 200-pound engine. It was further estimated that the planned machine would be able to fly 23 miles per hour with an 8 hoursepower engine driving propellers able to produce 90 pound thrust when rotating at 330 revolutions per minute. It is only logical to ask how the Wrights arrived at

2. Preliminary goals

these particular estimates, and what the choice tells us about their understanding of aircraft design.

The weight estimate of 625 pounds appears to have been strongly influenced by their experience with gliders and was determined as shown in Figure 3. Here the airframe weight of 425 pounds includes the weight of an operator (Wilbur weighed 140 pounds, Orville 145 pounds) but does not include an allowance for the weight of an engine. The wing loading of 0.85 pound/foot^2 is for the manned airframe only and closely agrees with the wing loading of 0.83 pound/foot^2 used in design of their successful 1902 glider. The estimated engine weight of 200 pounds is from Orville's June 7 letter to George Spratt. When this engine weight is added to the weight of the manned airframe, the wing loading for the planned machine becomes 1.25 pounds/feet.^{2}

Once a reasonable weight estimate has been determined, velocity can be estimated by considering the machine to be in steady flight in calm air. Under such idealized conditions of equilibrium, lift equals weight and velocity can be calculated from the expression for lift. In the form used by the Wrights during design of their 1903 machine, these idealized conditions were written.

WEIGHT ESTIMATE

WING AREA X LOADING[1] = AIRFRAME WEIGHT

500	X	.85	=	425
ENGINE WEIGHT			=	200
TOTAL WEIGHT			=	625 lbs

1. with operator

3. Weight estimate

$$L = W = .0033 \, S c_l V^2$$

where V = velocity in miles per hour
S = total area of the lifting surface in ft^2
c_l = lift coefficient as determined from the Wrights' wind tunnel measurements on airfoil number 12.
.0033 = the Wrights' "air presssure coefficient" (Reference 9)

In designing their 1900 and 1901 gliders, the Wrights had estimated performance by expressing equilibrium in terms of the lift equation used by Lilienthal, Chanute, and others, that is,

$$L = W = 0.005 \, S c_l V^2$$

This expression contains the so-called Smeaton coefficient of 0.005 introduced by John Smeaton in 1752 and gives an optimistically high value for lift. As it turns out, the Smeaton coefficient was wrong, but it had gone unchallenged and uncorrected for some 150 years.

When the performance of the Wrights' 1900 and 1901 gliders did not live up to expectations, they at first questioned Lilienthal's data on which their design was based. But when wind tunnel tests showed Lilienthal's data to be essentially free from error they concluded the fault was in Smeaton's coefficient. To bring their performance predictions into closer agreement with their glider experiments, the Wrights substituted data measured during flights with the 1901 glider into the lift equation and calculated the more nearly correct coefficient of 0.0033.[1]

Since the lift coefficient, c_l, was known to vary with the angle of attack, the Wrights' velocity estimate can be determined by choosing an angle of attack range of from 2.5 to 7.5 degrees, which corresponds to the Wrights' gliding experience, and constructing the table shown in Figure 4. Using the Wrights' wind tunnel results for surface number 12, the minimum velocity in this angle of attack range is seen to be 23 miles per hour. This velocity represents a worst case condition corresponding to the velocity that had to be obtained for the machine to fly in the angle of attack range the Wrights' considered desirable.

For steady flight in calm air, equilibrium also requires thrust to equal total drag. The drag equation used by Lilienthal, Chanute, and others is written

$$D = 0.005 \, S c_d V^2$$

The form of this expression is identical to that of the lift equation but the drag coefficient, c_l, is used in place of the lift coefficient, c_l. Moreover, total drag is the sum of the drag attributed to the lifting surface and that due to the frontal area of the machine. In the form used by the Wright brothers, these equations are written

$$D = .0033\ Sc_l\ \frac{c_d}{c_l}\ V^2$$

$$D_f = .0033\ S_f c_l \frac{c_d}{c_l}\ V^2$$

$$T = D_t = D + D_f$$

The only new terms introduced are S_f, denoting the frontal area of the machine, which the Wrights estimated to be 20 ft², and the drag/lift ratio $\frac{c_d}{c_l}$. Wilbur and Orville Wright used this somewhat unconventional form of the drag equation simply because they did not measure drag directly in their wind tunnel measurements. Instead, they measured the drag lift ratio, $\frac{c_d}{c_l}$ (Reference 10). Constructing the table shown in Figure 5 shows the maximum value of thrust in the preferred angle of attack range to be 90 pounds. This also corresponds to a worst case condition for the angle of attack range of interest.

VELOCITY ESTIMATE

LIFT EQUATION

$$L = W = .0033\ S c_l\ V^2$$

$$V = \sqrt{\frac{W}{.0033\ S c_l}} = \sqrt{\frac{625}{.0033\ (500) c_l}}$$

α	c_l	V
0	.145	51.3
2.5	.311	35.0
5	.515	27.2
7.5	.706	23.2
10	.839	21.3

4. Velocity estimate

The Wright brothers' estimate of the power required is obtained by multiplying the total drag by the volocity. As shown in Figure 6, the maximum power required to fly in the preferred angle of attack range is 8 horsepower.

It is indicative of the Wrights' consistent exercise of sound engineering judgment that they chose to base design of their first powered machine on worst case conditions. Had they not done so, it is quite

THRUST ESTIMATE

DRAG EQUATION

$$D = .0033\ S c_l\ \left(\frac{c_d}{c_l}\right) V^2$$

$$D_f = .0033\ S_f\ c_l\ \left(\frac{c_d}{c_l}\right) V^2$$

$$D_t = D + D_f$$

α	c_l	$\frac{c_d}{c_l}$	V	D	D_f	$T = D_t$
0	.145	.263	51.3	166	6.6	173
2.5	.311	.138	35.0	86	3.4	90
5	.515	.105	27.2	66	2.6	69
7.5	.706	.108	23.2	68	2.7	71
10	.839	.118	21.3	74	3.0	77

5. Thrust estimate

likely the weight growth experienced during construction of the 1903 machine would have rendered it incapable of flight.

Loads

Many writers have claimed that the structural design of early aircraft had to be largely a matter of chance simply because no one, including the Wrights, had any real knowledge of flight loads. Supporters of this thesis contend analysis, if any, was limited. They further suggest that members were sized by the haphazard procedure of choosing the lightest possible member, judging proportions by eye, and then, by trial and error, replacing failed components with stronger members until satisfactory structural performance was obtained. While some early experimenters indeed did resort to trial and error procedures, it

POWER REQUIRED

$$P_r = D_t V$$

α	D_t	V	P_r	
			mile lbs / hr	hp
0	172.6	51.3	8854	23.6
2.5	90.0	35.0	3150	8.4
5	68.7	27.2	1869	5.0
7.5	71.0	23.2	1654	4.4
10	77.3	21.3	1646	4.4

6. Power estimate

would be a grave error to assume the Wright brothers were so inclined (Reference 11).

In contrast with other experimenters, Wilbur and Orville Wright do not appear to have worried much about loads. To them, a load factor (erroneously thought to be a factor of safety) applied to external forces in equilibrium with the weight offered a common sense solution to the problem. Guesses, backed by reasoning, still had to be made in order to account for the span wise distribution of lift. But once lift was reasonably apportioned the loads on individual components could be determined readily. It is quite likely the Wrights simply assumed lift to be uniformly distributed along the span. While this assumption is in error, it satisfied the load conditions required by a number of the methods of structural analysis subsequently needed.

Moreover, it simplified the task of estimating how much of the load was carried by the front and rear spars. In the wing cross section shown in Figure 7. W_r denotes the running load which for a uniform distribution of lift is nothing more than the total load on the wing divided by the span. Wilbur and Orville Wright were aware of biplane effect from their wind tunnel tests, but it is doubtful that they knew how much load was carried by each wing. Consequently, it is quite probable they simply reduced the load carried by the lower wing. For the purposes of this

work, the lower wing is considered to carry 85 percent of the load on the upper wing. Thus, the upper wing supports 340 pounds of the estimated total weight of 625 pounds. This gives a running load of 8.8 pounds/foot. By considering the running load concentrated at the center of pressure, the load carried by each spar can be determined readily.

Since the center of pressure changes with angle of attack, two cases corresponding to extremes of flight in the preferred angle of attack range are shown. In the first case, the center of pressure is located at the 30 percent chord line. This case corresponds to an angle of attack of 10 degrees. In the second case, which shows the center of pressure at the 50 percent chord line, the angle of attack is 2 degrees. For the worst case condition, in which the center of pressure is located at the 50 percent chord line, the rear spar of the upper wing is seen to carry 81 percent of the load.

Sizing of Wing Components

As mentioned earlier, engineering handbooks published in the latter part of the nineteenth century provided a convenient source for methods of analysis needed to size structural members. Although these methods were not always based on rigorous mathematical analysis, they were commonly used by nineteenth-century engineers and did result in answers of acceptable engineering accuracy. For example, the method shown in Figure 8 was recommended for use by bridge builders confronted with the problem of finding the vertical shear at the supports of a continuous beam uniformly loaded along its length. By multiplying the given coefficients by the running load on the beam and the distance between supports, the vertical shear at each support could be determined with surprising accuracy. Moreover, the method could be extended to include any number of supports in

SPAR LOADING

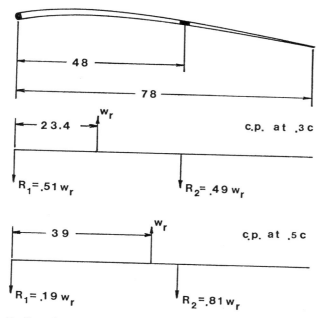

7. Spar loading

VERTICAL SHEAR COEFFICIENTS

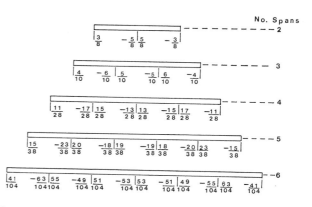

8. Vertical shear coefficients

the following manner: For a beam with an odd number of spans, like five, follow down a given line of coefficients, such as the line on the right hand end, and the coefficient is seen to be $^{15}/_{38}$. The 15 is obtained by adding the 11 of $^{11}/_{28}$ to the 4 of $^{4}/_{10}$. The 38 is obtained by adding the 28 of $^{11}/_{28}$ to the 10 of $^{4}/_{10}$. For a beam with an even number of supports, such as four, the end coefficient is seen to be $^{11}/_{28}$. Here the 11 is obtained by multiplying the 4 of $^{4}/_{10}$ by 2 and adding the 3 of $^{3}/_{8}$. The 28 is obtained by multiplying the 10 of $^{4}/_{10}$ by 2 and adding the 8 of $^{3}/_{8}$.

The origins of such questionable methods are a constant source of amazement but for a beam of eight spans, the results are within about five percent of those obtained by more exact methods. What is of importance to this work is that the problem is identical to that of finding the vertical shears on the spar of a biplane wing supported by interplane struts. Whether the Wrights resorted to the use of this empirical method or more exact, but mathematically cumbersome, methods is unknown. However, in passing it should be noted that this empirical method was still being used for aircraft design in Great Britain as late as 1917 (Reference 12).

Once the vertical shears on the upper and lower spars of a wing truss were known, the forces in all truss members could be obtained with the aid of a widely used graphical procedure known as Maxwell's Diagram. For the purpose of this work, a Maxwell's Diagram was used in conjunction with the vertical shears obtained by using the empirical method of Figure 8 to determine the force in each member of half the rear truss of the Wright machine. The external loads on the half truss, shown in the upper diagram of Figure 9, correspond to the equilibrium condition of steady flight in calm air at a two degree angle of attack. These loads were used to construct the force diagram shown in the lower part of Figure 9. The force in each component is indicated on the upper diagram with a letter suffix to denote whether the member is in tension or compression.

While construction of the Maxwell Diagram is straight forward, the tenets of truss theory preclude the method from providing any information on bending moments. These must be obtained by using an independent procedure, which, for a continuous beam with eight bays, would casually imply use of the Method of Three Moments. However, the Method of Three Moments is mathematically cumbersome and susceptible to arithmetic error when the calculations must be performed by hand. Consequently, an empirical method similar to that used for determination of vertical shear was often used by nineteenth-century engineers. As shown in Figure 10, the bending moment coefficients must be multiplied by minus $W_r l^2$, that is, the negative product of the running load

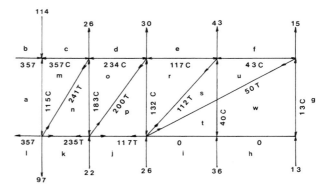

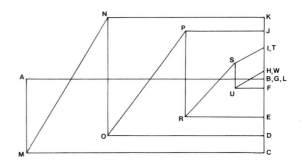

0   100
SCALE lbs

9. Determination of component loads

BENDING MOMENT COEFFICIENTS

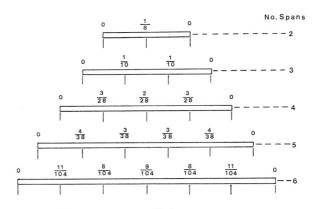

10. Bending moment coefficients

and the square of the support spacing, to obtain the bending moments. As in the case of vertical shears, the method can be extended to include any number of supports using the same arithmetic procedure previously described.

When used to determine the bending moments on the rear truss of the Wright machine, the procedure resulted in the bending moment diagram shown in

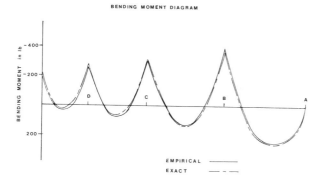

EMPIRICAL —————
EXACT   — — —

11. Bending moment diagram

WING SPARS

Column Load $\quad P_{cr} = \dfrac{\pi^2 E I}{L^2}$

Material $\qquad$ Spruce

$$E = 1.6 \times 10^6 \; psi$$

Let $\quad P_{cr} = 5P = 1800 \; lbs$

$$I = \frac{b h^3}{12} = \frac{P_{cr} L^2}{\pi^2 E} = .205 \; in^4$$

$$b = \frac{12 \, I}{h^3} = 1.5 \; in$$

$$b_a = 1.68 \; in$$

$$Margin = 5.6$$

12. Determination of spar width

Figure 11. An independent check of the bending moment diagram using the Method of Three Moments resulted in the curve plotted with a broken line and indicates the maximum moment of -389 in-lb is well within engineering accuracy. The letters A through D designate locations of the interplane struts.

In a biplane, the upper wing spars function as beams subjected to the simultaneous action of bending and compressive loads. Today's engineers are taught to be wary of such load combinations for, as the beam deflects due to bending loads, the compressive end load tends to interact, or couple, with the deflection so as to further increase bending. Although this behavior was understood by the late nineteenth century, the tendency was to regard it as a secondary effect. The cause of a number of early monoplane disasters can be traced directly to neglect of this "secondary" effect. But at any rate, it was generally conceded that with a suitable factor of safety the interactive effect would be negligible. Consequently, the usual approach taken was to consider the stress in the member to be made up of two parts; that due to bending and that due to the compressive load. This greatly simplified the task of estimating the dimensions of the cross section of the member.

Wilbur and Orville Wright appear to have neglected the coupling effect during detail design of the spars used on their 1903 machine. This conclusion is supported by the calculation shown in Figure 12 and is dependent on use of the governing equation in the form.

$$S = My/I + P/A$$

where S = total stress in the spar in lb/in^2
My/I = maximum bending stress
P/A = compressive stress
M = maximum bending moment in in-1b
y = half beam thickness = $h/2$ where h denotes span thickness
I = moment of inertia = $bh^3/12$ where b denotes spar width
P = compressive force in-1b
A = area of spar cross section = bh

For purposes of estimating the dimensions of the spar cross section it is convenient to simplify the expression to that shown at the right of the first line. Since the spar thickness, h, was set at 1.18 inches by the Wrights' choice of an airfoil and the spar location, the spar width, b, is the only unknown quantity in this expression. Thus, the spar width can be calculated directly by solving for b as shown on the second line. However, some explanation of how the values for bending moment, compressive force, and stress were selected so as to yield the indicated spar width may prove enlightening.

While at Kitty Hawk on September 23, 1900 (Reference 13), Wilbur wrote a letter to his father in which he states; "I am constructing my machine to sustain about five times my weight and am testing every piece." This often-quoted passage from the Wrights' correspondence has been interpreted by some writers to literally mean five times Wilbur's weight of 140 pounds. Such an interpretation is meaningless in design of an aircraft. A more meaningful implication is that the Wrights planned to use a factor of safety of five when designing their machines. However, what is now known as a load factor was often mistakenly called a safety factor in the formative days of aviation. The different meanings of these two terms was to remain more than mildly controversial until finally resolved in the 1920s.

The spars of the Wrights' 1903 machine were made of kiln dried spruce capable of sustaining a compressive stress of 6000 pounds per square inch. Reducing this value by a factor of 5 gives an allowable stress of 1200 per square inch and this reduced value was used in performing the calculation shown in Figure 12.

Wilbur and Orville Wright had an especially keen appreciation of material properties, as evidenced by their preference for West Virginia white spruce and second growth ash. Orville later wrote: "We figured we would get a slightly increased strength with the light spruce because with the same weight the cross section would be greater" (Reference 14). Such reasoning is flawless when it comes to design of compressive members like spars or interplane struts that can fail by buckling.

It may be recalled that the rear spar was estimated to carry 81 percent of the load when the center of pressure is at the 50 percent chord line. Calculations made using values of the bending moment and compressive force corresponding to this particular case yielded spar widths considerably smaller than the actual width of 1.68 inches. On the supposition that the Wrights' practical approach to problems may have prompted them to design the spar to carry the full load, the calculation was repeated using appropriate values for bending moment and compressive force. When used with the allowable stress of 1200 pounds per square inch mentioned earlier, this combination of values yielded the result shown in Figure 12 which agrees closely with the actual spar size used on the 1903 machine. The indicated margin of 7.3 corresponds to the design load factor for the spar when subjected to the reduced loading of 81 percent.

To further verify the meaning of Wilbur's statement to his father, it was decided to check the load factor used in sizing the rigging wire. This calculation is shown in Figure 13. In this case, the material was 0.091 in diameter hard drawn steel wire listed as having a breaking strength of 1300 pounds in several early handbooks. As shown in the Maxwell's Diagram of Figure 9, the maximum applied load carried by the truss wires is about 240 pounds. The design margin may be determined by dividing the breaking load by the maximum applied load. The margin of 5.4, corresponding to the design load factor, is seen to be in close agreement with the previous conclusion of 5. The difference can be attributed to the Wrights' choice of the nearest standard wire size that satisfied their requirements for safety. The next smaller wire

WING SPARS

$$S = \frac{M y}{I} + \frac{P}{A} = \frac{6 M}{b h^2} + \frac{P}{b h}$$

$$b = \frac{6 M}{S h^2} + \frac{P}{S h} = 1.69 \text{ in}$$

$$b_a = 1.68 \text{ in}$$

MARGIN 7.3

13. Load factor—Rigging wires

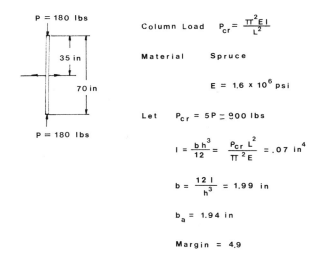

INTERPLANE STRUTS

P = 180 lbs

35 in

70 in

P = 180 lbs

Column Load $P_{cr} = \frac{\pi^2 E I}{L^2}$

Material Spruce

$E = 1.6 \times 10^6 \text{ psi}$

Let $P_{cr} = 5P = 900 \text{ lbs}$

$I = \frac{b h^3}{12} = \frac{P_{cr} L^2}{\pi^2 E} = .07 \text{ in}^4$

$b = \frac{12 I}{h^3} = 1.99 \text{ in}$

$b_a = 1.94 \text{ in}$

Margin = 4.9

14. Determination of strut width

size of .080 inches has a breaking strength of 1000 pounds, which would have reduced the design load factor to 4.2.

Wilbur and Orville Wrights' design treatment of the interplane struts on their 1903 machine provides a convincing example of their design ingenuity and familiarity with stress analysis. As shown in Figure 14, the gap between the upper and lower wings is 70 inches. Moreover, from Maxwell's Diagram the most highly loaded strut is seen to carry a compressive load of around 180 pounds. When such a long thin member is loaded in compression it can fail, without warning, by what is known as column buckling. Since the interplane struts on the 1903 machine function as long columns, their design is governed by an equation that can be written.

$$P_{cr} = \frac{\pi^2 EI}{L^2}$$

where P_{cr} = Critical load at which failure is imminent pound

E = Elastic modulus psi (For spruce $E = 1.6$ million psi)

I = Moment of inertia in 4 = $\frac{bh^3}{12}$

b = Strut width in

h = Strut thickness = .75 in

L = Length of column in

The Wright brothers clearly realized that a 70-inch-long column would require a substantial cross section in order to sustain a load of 180 pounds without failing. But a column of sufficient size would add weight and increase drag. Consequently, they sought an alternate solution.

Midway between the upper and lower wings of the 1903 machine is a horizontal wire in the plane of the front spars. It passes through the center of all highly loaded struts and is wrapped and sized at the points of entry and exit. The function of this wire is to stabilize the struts against lateral deflection and thereby increase the allowable column load. In effect, the wire halves the strut length and increases the load factor to 4.9, a value consistent with the Wrights' design criterion. A second wire in the plane of the rear spars stabilizes the rear struts and results in a comparable advantage. The fact that none of the struts failed during the Wrights' proof-of-concept flights in the gusty winds of December 17, 1903, attests to the effectiveness of this design solution.

Concluding Remarks

This article has attempted to shed some light on how Wilbur and Orville Wright went about design of the Flyer. Wilbur, the self-appointed spokesman of the two, had planned to publish a description of their design procedure, but his untimely death from typhoid in 1912 left that task undone. Consequently, it has been necessary to reconstruct their approach to aircraft design. To add credence to this reconstruction only information extracted from *The Papers*, from engineering handbooks published prior to 1900, and from engineering drawings donated to the National Air and Space Museum by the Orville Wright Estate was

used. The close agreement of all numerical results with evidence extracted from these sources suggests the Wrights used methods at least comparable to those presented here. It was particularly encouraging to note that none of the methods required a facility with mathematics beyond that normally acquired at the high school level.

The Wrights' ability to prepare realistic design estimates reveals a fundamental appreciation for the way aerodynamic, propulsive, and structural considerations interact during aircraft design. Their understanding of this interplay enabled them to set attainable goals for power, thrust, and weight that served to guide them along an otherwise uncertain path. Moreover, their recognition that under idealized conditions flight loads could be approximated by considering the external forces to be in equilibrium with the weight eliminated the need for resort to trial and error methods for sizing structural components.

By today's standards the 1903 Flyer indeed was a most marginal machine, but it was not the product of chance or of tinkerers popular legend would have us believe. As this work indicates, the Flyer was a consequence of practical men endowed with extraordinary engineering perception.

Notes

1. It should be noted in passing that the lift equation in current usage is

$$L = \frac{\rho}{2}(Sc_l V^2)$$

where ρ = free air density in slugs/ft^3

V = velocity in ft/sec

At the sea level conditions of the Outer Banks, ρ is approximately 0.002377 slugs/ft^3 so that this expression may be written

$$L = 0.001188\, Sc_l V^2$$

The lift equation used by the Wrights was written

$$L = 0.0033\, Sc_l V^2 \text{ with } V = \text{velocity in mph}$$

Converting the units of velocity to ft/sec gives the Wrights' equation in the form

$$L = 0.0033(3600/5280)^2 Sc_l V^2 = 0.001534 Sc_l V^2$$

which is in remarkably close agreement with current use. Doubting Thomases who believe the Wrights were tinkerers may find a moment's reflection on this agreement enlightening.

Howard S. Wolko graduated from the University of Buffalo as a Mechanical Engineer and holds a D.Sc. in Theoretical and Applied Mechanics from George Washington University. He served as a research engineer in experimental mechanics with Cornell Aeronautical Laboratory, a stress analyst and Head of Structures Research with Bell Aircraft Corp., Head of Solid Mechanics with the Air Force Office of Scientific Research, and was Chief of Structural Mechanics and Reentry Structures with the Office of Advanced Research and Technology, NASA. He also was Professor of Mechanical Engineering at Texas A&M University, and was Professor and Chairman of the Mechanical Engineering

Department at Memphis State University. He currently is Special Advisor for Technology to the Aeronautics Department of the National Air and Space Museum.

Dr. Wolko is a member of Pi Tau Sigma, Sigma Xi, the Society for Engineering Science, and the Society for Experimental Stress Analysis. He is listed in *Who's Who in the South and Southwest* and *American Men and Women of Science*. He has published numerous technical papers.

References

1. Wright, Wilbur, and Wright, Orville. *The Papers of Wilbur and Orville Wright, Including the Chanute-Wright Letters and Other Papers of Octave Chanute.* Edited by Marvin W. McFarland. 2 vols. New York, 1953. Hereafter referred to simply as *The Papers*.

2. *The Papers*, vol. 1, p. 102.

3. Bisplinghoff, R. L. *The Structural Engineering Practice of the Wright Brothers,* in *Aeronautica*, Fall-Winter, 1956.

4. *The Papers*, vol. 1, p. 54.

5. *The Papers*, vol. 1, p. 44.

6. *The Papers*, vol. 1, p. 290.

7. *The Papers*, vol. 1, p. 313.

8. *The Papers*, vol. 1, p. 386.

9. *The Papers*, vol. 1, p. 135.

10. Baker, M.P., *The Wright Brothers as Aeronautical Engineers*, Annual Report of the Smithsonian Institution, 1950, p. 215.

11. Judge, A. W., *Design of Aeroplanes*. London: Sir Issac Pitman and Sons, 1917, p. 156

12. Ibid, p. 131.

13. *The Papers*, vol. 1, p. 26.

14. *The Papers*, vol. 1, p. 1106.